SURGEON'S APPRENTICE

SURGEON'S
APPRENTICE

Theodora Koob

J. B. Lippincott Company
Philadelphia and New York

Contents

Contents

SURGEON'S APPRENTICE

I.

An Unhappy First Attempt

THE excitement of spring hung suspended everywhere: in the twitter of birds, in the green haze of birch and willow strands swaying in the gentle post-dawn breeze, in the steamy breath of the dew, in the heart of the boy as he lifted the yoke with the buckets slopping. The pump handle was at the blacksmith's—he had to carry water from the old well behind the barn, and he was happy to do it that bright morning.

No one was in the kitchen. Cora was still in her cabin, Launa milking. The boy unhooked the buckets carefully at the doorstep and laid the yoke upright against the house. Softly he carried in one bucket and set it carefully upon the pumiced-oak basin stand, where it would be handy. The kitchen always had such a clean, scrubbed look at five o'clock in the morning before anyone had come down. It even smelled clean, from the pine oil Launa used Saturdays for scouring the wide-planked floor. Fourteen Windsor chairs stood stolid about the huge maple table; pewter serving pieces gleamed in their cupboard racks; a fire was laid in the brushed hearth, ready for lighting. It would normally have been lit, but the doctor had gone out before daylight. Gregory could light the fire but he did not presume to do it, though the flint lighter lay ready on its protruding brick shelf. After all, Greg's father had given him specific directions when he had waked him: "Get fresh water in the surgery and kitchen, run the ponies into the back pasture, since there's no school, open the shutters in the hospital room and let in some fresh air, set the roan into the chaise in case I must send back for a patient, saddle the bay mare!" Gregory had done these commands in reverse order, for he knew what his father expected. He brought in the last bucket of water.

No rustle of awakening stirred anywhere. Gregory was at liberty to enjoy the new day, at least until Cora called breakfast or the doctor returned, whichever happened first. He closed the kitchen door quietly and started running past the kitchen garden toward the stable. He skidded to a sudden stop, remembering the yoke against the house; he turned back. Anything he neglected or forgot, his stern father punished severely. He grabbed at the yoke and swung it over his shoulder and bolted into the barn to hang it properly on its hook.

"Mornin', boy!" Launa greeted from the milking stool. She would draw just enough milk for breakfast, then her boy Arne would finish the milking.

Gregory swooped around Launa's right side and scooped up a palmful of warm milk from the pail and slobbered it. Launa kicked at him with her wooden barn patten and growled cheerfully, "Drat you—git, you spoiled brat!" Everyone liked Gregory, and he knew it! Save for his father, he might have been royally spoiled, youngest of nine strapping boys as he was. He went out of the barn, suddenly thoughtful, his bright, open face sober—he was a boy who slipped from mood to mood lightly as a fiddler drawing upon his instrument; his thoughts were like a bow upon his even features, his wide, rather thin-lipped mouth, his straight little nose, his gun-gray eyes under level black brows.

Arne came into the barn, still tying a rope through his breeches loops; he kicked up a stool from the corner between the end stall and the feed bins, caught it left-handed, and pulled down a clean pail from its hook to boot. He slapped Merrylegs in the first stall so that he could get beside her.

"Mornin', Massa Greg, goin' be beautiful today," the colored lad offered politely.

Gregory nodded, skipping out almost childishly. He took a swift look to the left down the drive and listened a moment, hoping his father was not yet riding in. He found neither sight nor sound of a horseman, so he began running. Beyond the kitchen garden and the gooseberry bushes, mulberry trees stood neatly lined; then a little brook trickled from a natural spring in a rocky knoll. Not many families had a whole brook starting in their backyard and running off on a gently circuitous course through meadow and pasture to where a spindled fence marked the Donlewis property line. There had been seven or eight other owners of the brook before Gregory's time, but he had sole rights now; he was king in the children's domain at their house, when his father spared him from the surgery!

The boy stepped tenderly across the brook and followed it along its farther bank. He stopped twice to test the water with a forefinger. It was cold! Finally, at the drip hole in the little knoll, Greg made a cup of his palms and sucked up the good-tasting water as a horse drinks, thrilling interiorly at its deliciousness. Not that their well and pump water were not both from the same underground source and equally tasty—but there was just something about the fresh morning, the infrequent liberty of the moment, the personal privacy, that made him feel an important part of the whole world. He sat cross-legged on a cushion of dry leaves that he had fashioned under an overhang of the knoll, a jutting edge of rock. Here in this secret place he came to sit, to think, to study when he had to memorize something difficult like a declension or a passage from Cicero or Horace. He mused now, chin in hand, elbow on knee, remembering things gone by. He had only recently begun to work for his father, after the accidental death of his oldest brother Guy, who had been a surgeon, too. Before that Gregory had been in his father's surgery only once, when he had broken his leg at five, and he had marveled at how quickly his father had set it, somehow keeping him interested the while in the splint and its wrappings. Then, shortly thereafter, he'd lingered after the removal of the splint and watched the surgeon sew up a badly injured hand. His father had quite literally tossed him out of the surgery when he noticed him watching, yet Greg had dared to peek again at an operation—he didn't care to dwell long upon the result of *that!* His early memories of his father were all the same—the surgeon had always seemed an awesome stranger.

Thinking all this, Gregory yet listened for the sound of a horse. The moss around the edges of the pool from which the brook was created was greening and looked like velvet under the first touch of sun that broke over the top of the knoll. Wild crocuses pushed their lavender-and-white noses out of the red Virginia clay, and above them laurel stems reddened with sap and their leaves glossed with the interior tonic of spring.

Then a halloo from near the house broke the quiet, and a white shirt and green breeches raced from the kitchen-way toward the drive gates. That would be Keith to open the gates for the doctor and take his reins. If Dr. Donlewis needed the chaise and medicines—Greg ran!

"I'm right here, sir!" he gasped, sliding to a stop, panting, just as his father tossed his reins to the waiting Keith.

"A half-dozen ready hands on a fair day," the surgeon laughed, for Arne, too, had come hustling from the barn.

"Walk her and rub her down, Keith," he nodded from lad to horse as he swung himself off.

"Must you go back?" Gregory inquired.

"No, 'twas just a fine new baby for Riggers."

"They called you?" Gregory asked, surprised. He knew already that women seldom called a doctor to help with bornings unless something went wrong. He knew, too, that his father had a reputation for being good in such cases and was sneered at for it by many fellow surgeons. "Midwifery's not surgery!" these high and mighty doctors claimed; but Stephen Donlewis went out when he was called, and sometimes when he wasn't.

Shaking his head at Greg's question, the doctor said, "No, Red Manthy did." She was the midwife up Coal Mines way, Gregory knew. "She thought there might be some trouble, but actually it went well enough." The doctor slipped his saddlebags off into Greg's reaching hands. "Anyone waiting?"

"No, sir." Gregory knew he'd have been called from the brook if any patients had come, for it was his responsibility, now that he was his father's apprentice, to make prospective patients as comfortable as he could. He took the saddlebags in through the waiting-room entrance.

His father came in at his back. "Good. After you put up the bags, go unhitch the roan from the chaise and we'll have breakfast."

Gregory went through to his father's study and took instrument case, traveling medicine box, and leather pouches for bandages from the thick saddlebags and set them all in their proper places; then he folded the bags on the particular shelf where the doctor always kept them handy. It had taken the surgeon years to achieve the silent, smooth efficiency in which he lived every day, the boy knew. The study had been added onto the main house along with the big hospital room that boasted ten cots. Once there'd been a shed where the study was, and the waiting room, narrow and unsatisfactory with its large fireplace that had crowded Dr. Donlewis's big desk against the window, had had to suffice as study too. Now the waiting room was quite comfortable, with old chairs that the doctor had collected at country auctions and set casually before the fire. There was even a convenient couch for the very ill or badly injured arrivals.

As the doctor came in, he shed his traveling cape and his old workaday tricorne for Greg to hang up; he struck a spark to the laid fire and stood a moment to watch it take.

"Should I have started the fire?" Gregory asked shyly —he was always tense with his father, afraid of doing too much or too little.

"Did I so command?" Stephen Donlewis asked sourly.

"No, sir."

"Well, then? You did fill the kettles," he had already made sure of this by sticking his finger into the spouts. "Loose the chaise and roll it back against the wall and take Sultan out to pasture with the ponies. I'll be in kitchen." The surgeon strode away from the crackling new fire, fighting hard against his limp, which Gregory supposed he hated since he always took long steps to hide it.

Cora was up now and had already made gingerbread; its redolence filled the big kitchen and choked Gregory with pleasure the moment he pushed in the door. The doctor was eating a chunk of the gingerbread, warm and gobbed with butter. He had finished the two slices of cold ham that he ate every morning; his steaming black coffee sat before him. He shoved the platter of ginger-bread toward Greg and poured him a mug of thick milk from the brimming pitcher. Cora brought the boy ham.

Gregory recognized his mother's step in the passage, then her bright voice addressed his father first.

"You're back, Steve! I heard you leave; it was scarce light."

He told her about the baby as she sat down to the coffee and hot bread Cora brought her. He told her something else that both interested and concerned Gregory.

"I've decided to take the two students from Hampden-Sydney after the semester ends this spring; one wants to go to Kentucky and one to Philadelphia. I can use the money before next winter; they're to pay cash in advance," the doctor announced.

"You won't find two hard with all the plantations?" Margaret Donlewis wondered. The doctor had five plantations and quite an area of county to serve, especially since he had taken over his son's practice after the young man's tragic death; in addition, Dr. Donlewis had a reputation for being excellent with fractures and lithotomies (operations for kidney or bladder stones)—he was busy enough!

"I've the boy," the surgeon nodded at Gregory, who munched his ham and gingerbread in an effort to be politely disinterested in his parents' conversation, though his heart somersaulted at the gratifying intimation that he might prove useful. His father continued. "He may as well learn early to work hard; since there's no school this week, I shall take him with me on my rounds and let him try his hand a bit."

At this exciting development the boy's pulses beat fast. His mother leaned over and pulled one of his curls, teasing, "See now, he's taking my baby away and I shan't have him ever again."

Greg made a wry face and the doctor frowned also upon such sentimentality and put an end to it by gestur-

15

ing his son after him into the surgery. "Finish bottling that cough syrup I made up last night; rinse out the towels and get them out; then I'll want you to deliver two packets of pills and get back in a hurry, for I expect old Caruthers at ten o'clock."

Caruthers, who had a kidney stricture, came for treatment weekly. He was crotchety to the point of being mean, and Gregory would have to stand and read *The Enquirer* to him to take his mind off his troubles while the surgeon treated him. The boy went to work willingly enough in the narrow, closetlike room that was his father's apothecary shop. He poured the rather pretty cough syrup from its big bell jar through a brass funnel into twelve small bottles, for which he then cut corks carefully from the big sheet of cork his father kept over the workshelf. He spilled only a drop or two of the syrup and scooped it up on his finger; it tasted like cherry. Sometimes his father made cough syrup taste like sassafras; Gregory liked both kinds himself! He labeled the bottles carefully, pasting on small white squares stating:

COUGH SYRUP
2

one spoonful
every two hours

Finished with that, he lugged the big pail with yesterday's soiled but salvageable cloths, towels, and bandages outside, where he scrubbed them thoroughly in the big wooden brassbound tub reserved particularly for the doctor's use. Gregory hated washing the "rags," as he termed them, but he had to do it every day even if it rained. The vinegar solution in which he soaked and rinsed them cut the unpleasant odors of stale blood and other excrement, but if one used it too strong, it could

16

burn one's hands raw. Gregory oiled his hands afterward with olive oil as he admired his handiwork flapping on the gooseberry bushes in the gentle April breeze. A day like this saved time—he did not have to secure his laundry to one of Launa's clotheslines; the squatty bushes served him well. He kept rubbing more oil on his hands and arms and sucking in the bright sunshine, until sharp fingers pulled the lobe of his right ear and he lost his left foot entirely.

"Off with you; 'tis no day to stand idle like a Stoughton bottle!" his father roared, tumbling the two boxes of pills into his hands.

Gregory ran most of the way, especially coming back, for the village clock in the new Cross Roads church tower had marked ten minus the quarter when he put the second box of pills on the counter of the Fairville general store for the storekeeper's wife. But Mr. Caruthers had not come when Gregory got back. Instead the doctor had set a whiny little girl with a bad whitlow on her right little toe upon his high operating table. The child's silly mother kept saying things that were frightening the little girl. In fact she was demanding over and over again whether the thing needed to be lanced. Greg knew his father was going to lance the toe because Dr. Donlewis had set a small pile of clean linen behind him on a low stand, the single drawer of which held his most frequently used scalpels.

"Talk to her!" the surgeon muttered to his son as soon as Greg came through the railing gate that separated surgery proper from waiting area.

Greg knew the little girl. "Sary, what you crying for? Bitty baby!" he admonished.

She snuffled back her sobs at the taunt and protested, "I'm five!"

"Don't act so! Bitty baby!"

The doctor swabbed the toe with vinegar-soaked cotton as the small girl stuck her tongue out at Gregory. The boy took an apothecary scale from the stand and set it on the end of the operating table and began to tinker with its balance.

"What's that?" Sary demanded.

"A scale. See these little weights? If I put one here like this and two others here, so, it will swing gently up and down, balanced; watch! But if I add another tiny one here, 'twill be too heavy."

"Let me do it, Gregory!" Sary begged, fascinated by the tiny brass gram weights.

Gregory gave her one, and as she reached to put it into the minuscule right tray of the scale, the doctor's sharp scalpel flashed across the toe. Sary squeaked, belatedly.

"That's a good big girl!" Greg admired, taking her hands as his father swabbed the wound. The child sniffled and a few big tears crawled down her cheeks, but she didn't carry on. After the doctor had tied up the toe and dismissed the child and her mother, he grinned over at his son.

"An adept distracter, aren't you? Next time perhaps I'll amuse the patient and you can cut, eh?"

The boy withdrew a little, casting down his eyes. His parent noticed and caught at his left arm hard, indicating that he had understood his son's withdrawal. "You have to start sometime, you know, boy! You've got to learn to do it! On easier things, the sooner the better. That's why I shall take you along this afternoon to the slave quarters. If there's some strong fellow with a simple case like that, you'll make the slash, hear?"

Gregory gulped. He had a tightening in his whole body about making an incision in anything alive; he wanted to do it but he couldn't. He'd had a hutch of rabbits that had been Guy's, the surgeon brother who had died; Greg had dissected them easily enough once they were dead, but he could not cut one living, even to save its life. His father knew! The boy supposed the cool-headed, smooth-fingered surgeon could not understand. In the midst of his troubled thinking, old Caruthers knocked. Greg let him in.

After lunch the day proved as glorious as the morning had promised. Greg loved to ride with his father down the shady river road, first to Merryhaven, his rich uncle Philip's huge estate. The surgeon rode magnificently and hard, since he had been a captain in the light horse during the War for Independence. Gregory had to switch his spotted pony to keep even. Trees were not enough in leaf to keep the sun from the road, and very soon father and son, laughing together, had to loosen jackets and cravats. They rode into the plantation by a back way, directly to the quarters. Gardeners and field hands looked from their work and waved at the doctor's familiar figure. And in the first cabin, where the doctor found a fracture case, the victim's wife smiled sweetly at Greg and remarked, "Got you another young gentleman doctor, Massa Steve?"

"My youngest boy, Lula; Gregory's his name," the doctor explained.

"Looks mighty like Massa Guy, don't he?"

This was true and everyone said it. "Yes," the surgeon agreed, looking thoughtful, while a lump rose in Greg's throat.

The boy soon busied himself laying open his father's things and running for splints and bandages, for the doctor kept such things on hand at each plantation in an outbuilding he had appropriated during the long years of his service. Greg did other things: when a patient had to be strapped down, he fastened the buckles; he handed instruments and threaded needles; a recent achievement, of which he was justly proud, was the permission to tie off a suture now and then. But he could not push the curved or straight gold, silver, or steel needles through the flesh any more than he could make an incision with the sharp knives. He had seen brave patients shudder under their pain and heard them scream often enough. His father's hands remained steady as though he were both deaf and nerveless. Gregory wanted to doctor and he knew that pain was something every surgeon had to understand. If only there were ways to prevent it or to relieve it!

Lula's husband was strong; he merely winced when the surgeon laid hold of the broken ends of bone and strained to get them together. Sometimes Greg's father had to reset a bone several times because a nervous patient upset his delicate work by inadvertent movement. Dr. Donlewis contrived a fine, strong splint in this instance, so that in a few weeks the man would be able to get about on crutches.

Later on the surgeon attended several cases of stomach complaint and one of fever, and lastly there was a hard boil on a man's ankle. This would be simple to open; the slave was big, handsome, strong as an oak. He actually smiled when the doctor handed his son his best Spanish scalpel and held the fellow's foot and calf with firm fingers.

"Go on, do it quickly as though drawing a very short, straight line on a picture; you need not worry about cutting too deep or too shallow, for there's naught but bone beneath; go on, boy!"

Gregory accepted the instrument and bent obediently over the man's foot. Then suddenly he felt terribly sick; he tossed the scalpel down on the cot and ran from the cabin. He stopped just outside, no longer seeing the pleasant afternoon sunshine; he stood with his arms pressed across his belly and his eyes fixed groundward. He remained thus for some minutes, then the doctor strode out and slapped him stingingly across the cheek with the palm of his hand. Tears started into Greg's eyes but he did not cry out.

"Go home!" Contempt laced the doctor's tone, contempt that actually stung much worse than his hand across the boy's face.

"I'm sorry I couldn't do it, sir," Greg whispered, but his father gave him no answer. Gregory found his way to his pony at the nearby hitching rail and set out for home, miserably unhappy with himself.

II.

Greg Makes Amends

IT was nearly suppertime when the surgeon galloped into the drive. Greg had busied himself in the apothecary room washing jars. He listened anxiously. Arne took the doctor's horse and in a moment Dr. Donlewis came through the waiting room and passed the pharmacy door without glancing at his son. Greg, feeling ashamed, wiped the jars he had so carefully scrubbed. He wished there had been an emergency to draw his father's attention from remembrance of the painful episode at the plantation, but only one person had stopped at the doctor's house to ask him to visit that night. Greg had made a note of this and put it on the big desk in the study. Soon he heard the sound of a pen scratching across paper and knew that his father had read the note and was now putting in his daily recordbook a brief half-English, half-Latin account of everything he had done on his rounds.

Presently Greg heard the surgeon's firm footfall outside the narrow apothecary room; the boy's stomach cringed under what he felt was positive disgrace.

"Come to supper, Greg," Dr. Donlewis called in as though nothing at all had happened, almost as though he had not been displeased. "Did you ever finish that sewing I set you?"

"Yes, sir," Greg pulled it from his own personal compartment under the pharmacy counter, the compartment his father had given him the very first day he had taken him as apprentice. In it Greg kept his own foolscap, inkpot and quills; his leather and canvas aprons; his clogs for running errands in bad weather; his notebooks, which his father ordered elaborately kept; his personal experiments, when he made any. He kept the compartment tidy against unexpected inspection by the surgeon, but he really liked things neat himself. He fetched out the fold of flannel now by touch, not having to look. He had practiced blanket, running, and intermittent stitches, all carefully made with silk suture thread and both straight and curved surgical needles. His father studied his workmanship and murmured, "Hm, I shall have to start you using catgut too," and no more.

They went to supper and it was good! Roast lamb and sugar-basted duckling, turnips, creamed potatoes, vinegared beets, fresh bread and sweet butter, and afterward sweet-potato pie with whipped egg whites and Merrylegs' creamy milk. Malcolm, Greg's oldest brother, came to supper. He often did, though he was a man grown and lived by himself in a log cabin that he was still building. Malcolm was always fun and told silly stories. Tonight Greg laughed too hard at his jokes because he was still uncomfortable about what had happened at the plantation. But his father mentioned nothing.

Afterward, when the surgeon had gone out on his call, Greg wandered about restlessly from kitchen to sewing room, where his mother was cutting shirts, and back again to flip soapsuds from the dishwater at Launa, who ordered him to scat in no uncertain terms. He returned to the sewing room.

His pretty, pink-cheeked mother whose soft brown hair was beginning to streak with gray, said, "Here, let me measure your arm, so I get the button band right. Why are you hopping about like a flea tonight?"

Gregory was proud of his new shirts, exactly like his father's. The surgeon had designed what he considered a practical garment for surgery, and Greg had been ready to burst with his own importance the day he was first sent to have such a shirt measured, for that meant he had been accepted into the inner sanctum of the surgery at last. Plain in front and buttoned down the back, the shirt had a simple, flounced cravat permanently fixed in front like a built-in jabot; the sleeves were full, with wide cuff bands that had two buttons so they could be fastened at the wrist or above the elbow. The doctor did not have to be bothered rolling up his sleeves; he could secure them out of his way, very practically.

"I—I—did—did—" Greg stammered, wanting to get the incident at Merryhaven off his chest to someone, "did Father—talk to you about—about what happened this afternoon?"

Mistress Donlewis searched her son's face. "What did happen?"

He told.

"You do truly want to be a surgeon, don't you?" she asked him.

"Yes, you know that I do," he swallowed painfully.

"I know what you're going to say, I have to learn to do it, cut——"

"Yes, all by yourself! Some things your father can insist that you do, but that is not one of them, and he understands it better than any of us," his mother told him. "Go on now to bed, 'tis coming late. It will all work out, you know. A year from now you will laugh about it."

He picked up a scrap of white flannel and ran it across his cheek. "I hope so," he said.

But he went upstairs instead of to his own room, which was beyond the sewing room, opposite the kitchen and just off the surgery. Light showed under the crack of his older brother's door. Gregory knocked. Keith was finishing his last year at school and preparing for college; he did not like to be bothered when he was studying, but it was vacation now, for a few days.

"Come on in—is't you, Greg?" Keith called.

Gregory was surprised to find Keith sitting on his bed, bathing his right instep in a basin of hot Epsom salts water.

"Redbug bite," the big boy explained. "It's got corrupted and hurts horribly; if it doesn't get better, it'll have to be cut open."

Gregory gulped, remembering sharply the man with the boil at Merryhaven. "Has Father seen it then?"

Keith grinned across at him. "You suppose I could limp without his noticing?"

They laughed together. Greg asked if he could do anything, but Keith shook his head as he poured more hot water into the basin.

"Are you sure it must be opened?" Greg wondered.

"Uh-huh, unless it opens of itself by afternoon; I can't afford to miss exams next week." He winced at the hot water.

24

"Keith, did you know Father was planning to take some students?" Greg asked.

"I heard him say so, yes. Why?"

"Nothing, but I was thinking perhaps they would need my room?"

Keith smiled, then winced again as he jerked the sore foot. "Don't worry, you can keep your room; they'll be together in the north bedroom—'tis plenty big enough. Why, I can remember when there were four of us in there! Go on to bed, Greg; 'tis nigh ten o'clock."

Greg took a candle and lighted it at Keith's; though a lantern always burned in the upper passage, it would be dark below if the surgery door were shut. Going downstairs softly, Greg listened and heard no one in the surgery. He set the candle on the little table at his bed, turned down his two patchwork quilts, took off his clothes and folded them neatly. It was nice not to have to take the morrow's recitations into bed with him and scan them a last time. He pulled off boots and stockings and got into his flannel nightshirt. He got into bed finally and rubbed his legs hard between the cool sheets to make himself a cuddly spot; then he took a deep breath and blew the candle out, taking a ridiculously long time about it until he was almost sick, holding back his breath. Afterward he fell asleep quickly.

His father woke him at six as usual. The surgeon was already shaved and dressed and had been working at accounts at his big roll-top walnut desk. Gregory lighted the fires in waiting room, surgery, and pharmacy and went for water as he had the day before, but there was no time for idling at the brook. The morning went fast; Greg cleaned out cabinets, rolled pills, and practiced sewing a set of double sutures, on tanned leather this time. It was slippery and hard to handle. Flesh, Greg supposed, could be hard to handle too; he gulped saliva just thinking of it. Then he considered that he might practice on himself. He took a thin, curved needle and resolutely pinched up the skin on his left middle finger, holding it with his thumb. He started to push in the point of the needle; it hurt! Tears started into his eyes and he promptly decided it was not the day for that sort of experimentation. Then he heard Keith with his father in the surgery.

"Gregory!" the doctor called.

Greg laid down his sewing, hurried into the waiting room and swung himself over the railing into the surgery on his hands, a practice his father frowned upon, though he said nothing at that moment. Keith, sitting on the big couch in the surgery, bit in his feeling as his father touched the hard, reddened area on his instep.

"I think we'll have to open this after lunch," Stephen Donlewis said. "Will you try, Greg, if I give you the chance?"

This was indulgence for his performance—or rather, non-performance—the day before, Gregory knew, and he tried to be eager to say yes, but his throat locked. He looked frantically at Keith.

"Sure, he'll do it," the bigger boy offered a warm vote of confidence.

"Well?" the surgeon waited.

Greg struggled to speak and no sound emerged.

"Go back to your work!" The same stinging contempt sounded in the doctor's voice now as on the afternoon before.

Gregory touched his cheek as if the sentence had been a slap. Back in the apothecary room he licked in a few salty tears of chagrin. After a bit Keith came hobbling by.

"You might as well experiment on your own flesh and

26

blood," he offered lightly; "I promise not to scream and I'll not sue you for any error!"

"Please, *please*," Greg pleaded, "I can't—I can't do it."

"He's not at all happy with you, which you know, I need hardly tell you!" Keith took a pewter basin and some clean cloths and went to get a kettle of hot water at the waiting-room hearth.

When Launa sent Gregory out to pick parsley a quarter hour before noon, the doctor was in the driveway, tightening the hub of a chaise wheel. With his shirtsleeves buttoned above his elbows and his legs braced, he was pushing upon a great vise while Tullah, their handy man, bore down on the axle. Greg stopped a moment, parsley in hand, to watch. Suddenly his father dropped the implement and swore beneath his breath, and then caught his right wrist hard in his left hand.

"There now, that's that!" he growled presently. "Keith's disabled for this sort of thing, so I hurt myself too!"

"Are you hurt bad, sir?" Gregory ran anxiously to his side.

"I don't know—go fix a basin of water, hotter than you'd care to touch yourself," his father directed.

Gregory stood handy while the doctor bathed his wrist in the hot water until his whole hand reddened like a cooked lobster; afterward, scorning his son's service, the surgeon bound the wrist tight with heavy linen, using his left hand and his teeth. Greg then made a sling of linen and Dr. Donlewis rested his arm in it and went thus to eat the noon meal. He mentioned to his wife that he was glad no operations were scheduled. Gregory supposed he had forgotten about Keith's foot; well, that wasn't exactly an operation.

"Hurts like the devil!" the surgeon observed as he ate

left-handed. "It should be all right directly. I could feel the confounded tendon pull," he half-laughed wryly.

Greg held his tongue about Keith. After lunch he had to deliver some packets of medicines. Returning around three o'clock, he found his father reading, sitting in one of his great leather armchairs. Noticing the boy, the doctor nodded.

"Get some clean bandage, a cupping basin—one of the little copper ones will do—and my small bistoury; then you may call Keith down," the doctor directed immediately. So he had not forgotten.

Gregory took as long as possible to lay everything ready; he wanted to goad himself into offering to make the incision, but he couldn't seem to get any words out of his mouth. His father ignored him. Keith came, limping quite painfully, after Greg called.

"Sit on the couch and put that towel folded double under your foot," the doctor said. "Blasted thing's still hard as a rock, isn't it?"

"Shall you need a suture, sir, afterward?" Gregory wanted to know.

"No, but get a small artery hook, for there'll be a core to pull." The surgeon pulled his arm from the sling and then twisted the cloth off. He buttoned his right sleeve above his elbow, but in trying to undo the left sleeve button, he frowned so painfully that Keith reached out to help him. Gregory got a hot-cold, sickish, and also rather guilty feeling in his gut.

"Give me the bistoury," the surgeon ordered. Greg put the instrument into his father's right hand. Dr. Donlewis's eyebrows knit; the small knife slipped; the surgeon winced and caught at it deftly with his left hand. Returning the bistoury to his right index finger and thumb, he warned Keith. "Grit your teeth—it'll hurt."

Gregory found himself wondering which of them it

would hurt more, his brother or his father. The doctor, still frowning, poised his right hand over the infected instep; then he fumbled again in his grasp of the bistoury and ground his teeth together. Greg, white and tense, thrust out his right hand.

"I'll try!" he cried intently. "I'll try, sir."

The doctor let him take the bistoury. Setting left thumb and index finger tight upon Keith's swollen foot, he directed Gregory. "Feel with your left index finger for the crown of the hard spot—feel it?" Greg nodded. "Balance your left hand behind mine. Now jab, don't slash; jab quickly to make a cut about as deep as your finger and no wider—go on!"

Keith grasped the couch sides and set his teeth; he didn't murmur. Gregory struck with the sharp instrument quite firmly. Pus jetted over his fingers from the incision before he could draw back. Keith parted his teeth in a voiced breath and gave a slight quiver.

"Take the artery hook and lift out that whitish block —hold the cut open! That's right," Dr. Donlewis continued directing.

Gregory dug in the hook and pulled gently and firmly; a hard core as long as his little finger came out on the artery hook. Keith sat quiet, staring, still gritting his teeth. The opening bled a little and oozed pus and lymph.

"Clean it with the mildest salt solution and bandage it lightly," the doctor said. He walked around the operating table in the middle of the room, lifted his right hand upon it and began undoing the knot that held the binding he had put upon his wrist. As Gregory bound up his handiwork on Keith's foot, the surgeon slowly unwound the heavy linen binder which he had previously soaked with wintergreen liniment. As Keith put his feet back into his knit house slippers, Dr. Donlewis tossed the binding into the bucket with dirty linen. He looked evenly across the operating table at his youngest son.

"So. You've made your first incision, boy," he offered gently.

Greg stared over at him; he tried not to cry, though mixed-up feelings were tugging at his self-control. "You —you didn't sprain your wrist?" he whispered.

"No," the doctor had wonderfully steady, piercing gray eyes. The boy lost his first quick feeling of resentment at having been tricked. "I rather thought you could come through in a crisis, boy! There's more than one way to skin a cat, you know." The surgeon's mouth twitched a little, but he would not give the boy the satisfaction of the broad grin that likely rose inside him.

III.

Two New Friends

THE holidays ran by too swiftly. Gregory watched Malcolm plow and plant their fields. Nights he experimented in the pharmacy with things his father allowed or explored the books in the surgery, having no lessons to prepare. It was a fine vacation, but Saturday Greg realized that it would soon be over. School would be all right too; he liked school and knew he was privileged in the one he attended. Bodewell's Academy was one of the best boys' schools in the state, perhaps in all the new states of the new country, which was, that April of 1811, twenty-three and a half years old—or you could say thirty-five, depending on whether you counted from the

Constitutional Convention or from Mr. Jefferson's Declaration of Independence.

Saturday afternoon he came back from the miller's, where he had taken a sack of barley to be ground into flour. Hanging over the surgery rail, he watched his father split sutures. "Sir—" he was formal with the doctor and never called him "Father" in the surgery; in fact, he scarcely thought of him, there, as a close relative but rather as a professional paragon to be imitated—"sir, how are babies born?" he demanded abruptly.

Stephen Donlewis looked up sharply and asked, "Surely you know?"

"Oh, I know they're born out of their mothers, but I mean, well, actually?"

"Have you not seen anything born? Rabbits, one of our calves?"

"Not rabbits nor a calf but mice—I saw mice being born once and one came out backside first and I helped it a little," Gregory admitted.

The doctor smiled. "So, 'tis good you did, perhaps; one must usually help out a baby that comes backside first, too. Babies are born like mice, really, though not usually so many of them at once, thank heaven!" he laughed. "You will get to see a delivery sometime at one of the plantations, I'm sure. What made you think of this today?"

The boy smiled at him wistfully. "The miller's retriever bitch had five pups today. I suppose that's what made me think of it. She was licking the last one clean when I got the flour sack from the hopper room."

Dr. Donlewis just murmured, "Oh," as his wife appeared to announce mealtime. "Put these sutures in the drawer and those on the table in my traveling case," he ordered Gregory after putting the neatly rolled threads in strips of clean linen.

31

Gregory scuttled to his place at the big maple table in the kitchen after everyone else was seated.

"Here I've raised nine boys and none has ever had a dog; I had a big shaggy dog of my own from the time I could climb a fence. Better run down to the mill, Greg, right after eating, and pick out one of those pups before Ed drowns them all. He won't mind letting Nellie nurse one if he knows you'll take it off his hands soon as 'tis weaned," the doctor said between spoonfuls of soup, as though he were discussing the most casual thing in the week's news. That was a wonderful thing about him, Gregory thought—when he surprised you, it was a veritable windfall!

Astonished, Greg sat staring, after dropping his soup spoon with a clatter and splashing the table so that Keith giggled.

"You did want one of those pups?" the doctor's level glance commanded Greg's attention.

"Yes, *sir!*" He knew exactly which one, the woolly brown one with the thin streaks of gold in the brown of its withers and around its collar. He gulped against the excitement that began beating like a new heart in the pit of his stomach. "I—I'll be mighty proud to have a pup, sir—Father," he whispered across the table, his cheeks flaming under his altogether happy embarrassment.

"You must care for it entirely and keep it from the surgery end of the house. For all of me it may be anywhere else if 'tis clean enough; arrange with your mother," his father stated flatly.

The next few weeks ran by posthaste. Dogwood burst into sparkling bloom on farm and in forest; crocus and jonquil pushed; the wheat rose high in Malcolm's fields. It was weather to hunt wild herbs and spices, to dig up moles in the kitchen garden, to press the coveys of bobwhite in their woods. Before he could believe it, the wonderful day came when Gregory's pup could slop its own food, and the boy brought it home triumphantly and made it comfortable in a box lined with old flannel at the bottom of his bed. Within twenty-four hours the pup graduated to the bed itself. The doctor, looking in one night before Greg had snuffed his candle, saw the dog whom Greg had named Tawny, snuggled on top of the patchwork quilt between Greg's knees. He smiled indulgently and Greg breathed easier. The dog could stay —if he behaved himself.

May all but exploded, it burst out so full of gay blossoms on roadside and in forest, on farm and in meadow. Riding to school every morning was sheer delight, with the sweet breath of honeysuckle on one side of the road and the trickling, chanting freshet on the other. Birds outdid each other singing, squirrels chattered noisily, the very plantation dogs banded together and carried on like puppies; jonquil and crocus gave place to bluebell and dogtooth; redbud leafed full and embroidered the brassy glare of noon with welcome shade.

Sometimes Gregory rode to school with Keith but often he went alone, usually earlier so he could take his time at crossroad and brook, at meadow and creek, stopping in a favorite spot to dig up a toad or stretching head-down to sip mint-flavored refreshment at some particular spring.

On such a morning, when Greg had set out as soon as he had finished his chores in the surgery, he heard the creek below his school grounds gurgling long before he reached the wooden bridge that crossed it and led directly to the iron gates of the academy. The absence of other boys on the sloping academy lawns and other ponies in the drive told Greg that he was truly early. He pulled his right rein and took his black-and-white pony into high grass at the roadside past a spot of fresh green huckleberry down an aisle between some young birch and ash trees to the water's edge, where he dropped the reins and gave the animal his head to drink. Greg dismounted and hopped from one stone to another out into the water, rolling pebbles across a flat boulder, grinning as they plopped and created circles in the clear creek. A crackle of branches caught the boy's alert ear and he faced around, startled.

Patches was still sucking softly, but otherwise there was thick silence as though things had deliberately hushed. It was *too* quiet; Gregory turned his body carefully on the boulder, lifted himself from his knees to stand erect, and looked back toward the road—nothing that way! He turned then left toward scrub growth, a nest of young alder saplings. Was there something or someone among the alders, something or someone holding painfully still —a raccoon, maybe? Greg stepped gingerly from the boulder by way of two other rocks and tiptoed onto the thick, mossy edge of the small stream just where the thicket began. In a few strides he was able to reach out and part the first of the stripling trees and look inside. It was thick and green within, like a little hideaway. Gregory blinked against the emerald haze, trying to focus.

"Git out o' here!" a hoarse voice shouted.

It was not a wild thing in the thicket, it was another boy: a scrawny, lean, and dirty boy who was sitting down, leaning his back hard against a fair-sized birch trunk.

Gregory had plenty of Donlewis spunk.

"Why should I? Do you own the place?" he demanded.

"Git, I say! I ain't wantin' no comp'ny," the fellow insisted.

"I'll walk through here if I like," Gregory returned with twelve-year-old confidence in his own prowess; a

34

glance had already told him that the strange lad was bigger than he but weakish; he had not moved from his position against the tree, and his left arm hung rather useless in a dirty and very likely bloodstained blue-cotton shirt sleeve. Gregory came on.

With a swift swoosh a knife flashed past Greg, missing him perhaps only because he had changed his course imperceptibly with his last step. The knife blade bit into a sapling behind. Gregory riled instantly and butted his head down to tackle the strange boy. The stranger pushed on his right palm, trying to get a grip with his left foot; quite suddenly he choked coarsely and fell heavily. Greg caught himself in his lunge by grasping at a young tree. He hung on a moment and stared down in awe at the other boy. The strange lad had fainted! He was lying on his back; his left shoulder was indeed stained with dried blood and dirt, and his right leg was tied clumsily to a piece of thick branch, tied beneath the knee with strips of what had been a dark-brown fustian jacket. Gregory felt his heart pound with new excitement. He could not go off to school and leave the other boy like that——— He felt in his breeches pocket for his handkerchief. He pushed his way between the young trees to the creek, and wet the cloth thoroughly. Coming back, he lifted the strange boy's head a little and wiped his face; he was careful not to touch the hurt shoulder. Upon a second application of the wet kerchief the lad opened his eyes.

"Water," he whispered, "I need water—I wanted to git to the water———"

Gregory carried his father's old Revolutionary canteen in his saddlebag against going thirsty on his rides back and forth. He ran to get it, filled it with the fresh-running creek water, and came back to the thicket.

The strange boy was trying to lift himself on his good hand. Greg held the canteen to his lips; the lad gulped the refreshment long and gratefully. Gregory set the vessel down and observed, "You need a doctor."

"Naw, I'll be all right now—thanks." The boy looked a bit ruefully at where his sheath knife still hung in the alder trunk. "I—I didn't expect no favors, after—well, I reckon I didn't welcome you none?"

"No, you didn't," Gregory grinned. He walked over to the tree and pulled out the knife. "You reckon 'tis safe for me to give it back to you?" he asked.

"Fer you, yes—I don't fergit when folks treats me decent," the boy answered.

"Where do you live?" Gregory inquired.

"Ain't tellin'," the lad responded. He struggled to sit up and winced from his sore leg.

"You need a doctor," Gregory repeated and then offered the information, "my father's one."

"I don't need nothin' and you keep your mouth shut that you saw me, hear? Or maybe I'll fergit that I owe you somethin'," the boy muttered threateningly, but he was miserably sick, Gregory could tell.

Observing carefully, as he had been taught to do when patients came into his father's waiting room, Gregory noted that the lad's leg seemed broken. He had run away, the doctor's son supposed: from a school, his family, a master? Greg could not hazard which. The lad had on fairly good but very dirty torn broadcloth clothes, breeches and shirt, his leather vest was in fair condition and such a one as might be sold in Richmond, Norfolk, Petersburg at market. His brown fustian jacket, which he had tied in strips around his bad leg, was the kind common among young apprentices at trades. Perhaps the lad had more likely run from a master than from school or family, for from his speech he was not much schooled. However, he was no mountain or back-country boy, for his soft slurring was rather typical of Chesterfield

County. He was incomparably dirty; Gregory all but winced at his soiledness. With a tacit question on his face the poor fellow reached out his good hand again, took up the canteen and emptied it, slobbering the water down.

" 'S good!" he admitted.

"Are you hungry?" Gregory asked with a boy's bluntness.

"Some," the lad said weakly.

"I've a bit of pone and some chocolate maybe, in my saddlebag," Gregory offered.

"And you don't want it yoursel'?" the boy tried hard not to appear hopeful of a negative reply.

"Of course not—I'll get what's there." He broke his way through the saplings and surprised Patches dipping his forelegs gingerly but pleasurably in the shallow water at the creek edge. Gregory scooped up the reins and looped them over a nearby branch for safety's sake. Boys were shouting to each other now on the slope that led to the school buildings; it was getting toward class time. Greg couldn't chance having to chase the pony upstream. Grabbing the napkin that contained his refreshments, the doctor's son hurried back to the stranger in the thicket. The boy ate ravenously.

"You ran away or something?" Gregory steered a direct course but discreetly, without anxiety, sort of lazily making inquiry.

But the boy returned his muttered "Ain't sayin'" swiftly as he licked his fingers of the last remains of the chocolate.

"You ought take care of yourself, at least; did you break your leg?" Greg pursued.

The strange boy had taffy-colored yellow hair caught at his neck in a bit of rawhide; his eyes were a striking blue beneath thin, straight, yellow brows; he was brown as a good saddle beneath the dirt but there was a kind

37

of pallor upon his skin, a hint of coming trouble, Gregory thought—where a bit of his right leg was exposed, it was bruised black and angry red above the injury, suppurating, the doctor's son knew. The lad nodded. "Yeah, I broke my leg; I was crossin' a stone fence and it give way and my leg got caught. I pulled hard to loose it and it snapped. It hurt bad—it still does. I tied the stick in place to hold it straight, but it don't do much good."

"The bone must be set together right, inside, the way it goes naturally. You must go to a doctor!" Gregory told him emphatically.

"Naw! I ain't goin' to no doctor; now lemme be!"

"And what will you do?" Gregory was practical to a fault.

"Go back to my . . . my . . . h–house—I done got one, ye know."

"Going to walk, eh?" the doctor's son taunted.

The boy's blue eyes reflected his physical and mental anguish then. "I . . . I cain't walk, but I got down here, most all the way to the water . . . when you come blunderin' in. I reckon I kin git back the same way, rutchin' along on my backside. . . ."

"I've a pony; might be I could manage to get you up on him, if you weren't so pigheaded about my knowing where you live! In fact I could come to see you at noon, maybe, and even bring you a bit of my lunch and some bandaging for your leg." Gregory offered all this flatly, with no particular show of enthusiasm; the boy must be approached slowly.

The lad searched Gregory's face hard, keenly. "You'll not tell nobody about me?"

"Not if you don't want me to, but I think——"

"Never mind what you *think,* just promise you'll not tell a livin' soul you seen me. You look like you'd keep your given word!"

Gregory promised, eager suddenly for this pact between them. Then he held out his right hand to the fellow. "Grab hold; then you can hook your arm around my neck and hop some on your left leg." Greg pulled the lad to his left foot slowly, cautiously, surely.

"My left shoulder's hurt too—cut. It bled bad, couple times, but 'tis stopped now," the boy confided. Then quite abruptly he asked, "Say, what's your name?" They were making headway through the saplings, though the progress in successive hops was painfully slow.

"I'm Gregory Donlewis and I live in Fairville."

"Ain't never heard of Fairville," the lad muttered.

"Well, that's not surprising. 'Tis mighty small," Gregory chuckled. "What's *your* name?"

"Bart."

"Bart what?"

"Ain't tellin'!"

Gregory immediately wondered if the Bart were made up, but probably it was not; the strange lad did not seem guileful, only apprehensive and furtive. He was taller than Gregory and wretchedly thin. He winced at each hop, for movement jerked at his bad leg and thumped at his sore shoulder. Patches came to meet them as far as his lead rein would allow. Bart could not lift foot to stirrup, but he did manage to throw himself bellywise across the saddle with a helpful boost from Gregory.

"Git goin' fast, heh? We're near the road now; ye kin go back through the huckleberry bushes there and then through a bit of lane-like leadin' into another thicket and up over the hill. The shack's there; I've a little shack on the down slope o' the hill," Bart directed.

"Hold onto the stirrup leather with your good hand a minute," Gregory called quickly. "I think you dropped something out of your pocket."

"What? What did I drop?" Bart asked.

With the fingers of one hand twisted in Patches's reins, Greg stooped and picked up the dirty little packet that had slipped to the ground when Bart had struggled across the flat of the saddle. Made of linen, the tiny sack seemed to contain something solid and metallic; its edges were sewn tightly shut with the clumsy stitching of a boy. Greg supposed that the packet contained money, perhaps all that Bart had in the world. He reached it out to the boy and said, "See, this!"

Bart pushed out his head and caught the sack neatly in his teeth and dropped it into his good hand. "Thanks. I don't want ter lose that," he clutched it hard along with the stirrup strap. "Let's git on now!"

Gregory led the pony gingerly. He knew about the shack; it had belonged to a man named Neever who had died some eight years ago. No one would look in that dilapidated shack for a runaway boy, likely enough; without prior knowledge no one would.

"Your paw's rich, eh?" Bart inquired as he hooked his right arm around Greg's neck again and slid down from the pony and began a painful hobble into the musty, decaying shelter.

The morning sun streaked in through a half-horned east window. In a corner stood a roped cot with a soggy corn mattress and a shred of dirty blanket; the boy had naught else of comfort save a broken chair and a cache of green apples. The surgeon's son stared aghast. In the light of such wretchedness, yes, his father was indeed rich! But he replied cautiously, "No, he's not rich but we've a good house and garden; my biggest brother farms; we're not uncomfortable."

"I reckon your school's mighty nice and comfortable too. I lay in here yestiddy and I could hear the boys at games 'cause the wind was comin' clear across creek and up hill." Bart dropped upon the misshapen mattress with a sigh. Carefully he stuffed his cloth packet in the square pocket on the front of his ragged shirt. Gregory wanted desperately to help the poor fellow but he could only stand rather starkly and inefficiently by, not feeling free with the lad nor with his own capacity to help.

"I must go now or I'll be late," he said. "I'll try to come back and see you at noon, if you like? We've more than an hour because we've a study period after lunch. We're not supposed to cross the hedge line out of the academy grounds, but I might be able to get through and across the creek without being seen."

"If ye come, scratch thrice upon my door, eh?" Bart suggested. "And thank ye kindly, Greg Donlewis, for what ye've done," he whispered and then he turned his face to the wall, not wanting to see the friendly Gregory go.

IV.

Trouble Brews

OUTSIDE the cabin Gregory swung himself into saddle with an acute sense of pity. He thought of the boy all morning long; Bart's tawny hair and poignant blue eyes rose out of the mathematics text, danced upon the wall maps. The musty bed, the murky, dusty one-room cabin, haunted Greg. He was simply compelled to go back after lunch; he was actually compelled to more than that! He managed to scratch his arm so hard that it bled, during the midmorning study period that the Greek master gave the good students that bright sunny day. Gregory made a ridiculous fuss over the scratch, claiming he had tripped and sprawled upon a dirty branch of rose thorn and insisting that his father preached cleanliness. This, in a sense, was true, for Doctor Donlewis did have a reputation for scrupulous cleanliness, something most of his colleagues derided. One of the serving maids finally obliged by binding up Greg's arm elaborately in some strips of torn sheeting. And at lunch time Gregory slipped his bread into his pockets along with two strips of bacon and a baked potato. He got up from table with his cinnamon tart in his hand; this was forbidden, carrying away food, but since Gregory was one who generally never erred, the proctor at his table didn't notice.

The bright day had become hot and scintillating. The students dispersed in small groups or singly to study for their afternoon recitations. Gregory wandered languidly down the east garden slope into a pleasant clump of neatly trimmed laurels. Luckily no one else was there, though the spot was a favorite with many boys. He brushed his way carefully between two laurels on the outer circle of the clump; then, taking quick reconnaissance that there were no boys who could sight his escape, he ran swiftly, his heart beating painfully, across a patch of open lawn. He leaped over the carefully trimmed box hedge that separated the academy grounds from the creek.

Once beyond the hedge, Gregory ducked down and crept the several yards to the creek bank, where he was sheltered by scrubby underbrush. He dared not waste time going down to the bridge. He stripped off boots and stockings, tucked them between two rocks for safekeeping, and waded into the creek at a spot where he knew it was shallow and had steppingstones clear across. Minnows shot between his legs; the water was startlingly cold, refreshing. Coming out upon a flat stone near the far bank, Greg curled his toes a second, enjoying the warmth where the sun had been beating down. Then he hurried up the hillside and over its crest and scratched three times upon the worn door of the run-down cabin.

"Greg Donlewis?" Bart's hoarse voice came in response to the third signal.

"Yes!" Gregory pushed the door in. It was now fairly light in the cabin as the noon sunlight filtered through sundry cracks and breaks and the one sad window. Gregory could more readily see how sick the strange lad was. His tan lay like a coating upon his pallor; he was shivering but he tried to smile.

"I thought you weren't comin'; I've no notion o' time, y'know," Bart murmured.

"I've brought you a bit of lunch," Greg took out the rather crumpled bread and meat and potato, and laid the cinnamon bun on the bed.

Bart ate hungrily, savoring the crumbs of bacon particularly. " 'S good," he muttered. "I bin eatin' them green apples and they—well, they're only good fer one thing, ef'n ye know what I mean, an' in my condition 'tweren't no fun wantin' ter run outside every hour!"

Gregory had to laugh, though he had no doubt that the lad had been miserable. "Tomorrow I can bring you some real food," he offered, "if I can get to linger in the kitchen after supper. I work for my father in his surgery, and he's strict! You've got to eat while your leg heals. Oh," he began unwinding the strips of bandage from his arm, "I pretended and inveigled this from one of the servants for a start. I can get better bandage at home, and maybe some ointment; if Father uses any and the jar's open, I can scoop some out on a bit of brown paper, but I daren't take it else, you understand? 'Twouldn't be right exactly—'twould be stealing from my old man, so to speak."

Bart wrinkled his pain-drawn mouth into a half-smile

43

at this rather fine distinction in righteousness, but then he burst out, "You oughtn't be doin' all this; you might could get into real trouble, too. I bin layin' here thinkin' I wish I wasn't in it—trouble. . . ."

"Can't you tell me? Maybe telling will make everything better; maybe you only think you're in trouble."

The strange boy set his teeth and Gregory knew better than to pursue his queries. The doctor's son set about unwrapping the strips of torn jacket from the leg Bart had broken. He took away the dirty branch and examined the limb; it was horridly purpled with bruises and caked with blood and dirt; an inadvertent movement bumped the lower portion and Greg could hear the grind of the broken bone. "I—I don't know very much about a thing like this," Greg admitted as he began washing the leg carefully with a bit of rag and the creek water from his canteen. He had watched his father set fractures several times, but he had never done any more himself than wind stripping about the final cast or splint after the surgeon had the wrapping well started. "I'll just try now to get it clean and then tie it up. Tomorrow if I can bring enough bandaging and a good set of splints, I'll try to put it together right for you . . . if . . . if you can stand it," he offered.

"Reckon I've got to stand it—it hurts all the time anyhow," Bart acknowledged. "I—I found your kerchief; you dropped it this morning going out. I put it on the cut in my shoulder and the wetness felt good," the lad went on.

Greg worked carefully on the leg, trying not to cause his new acquaintance any unnecessary pain. He worked so slowly that time ran away from him. Finally he left the cabin. When he reached the opposite bank of the creek, as he knelt to put on his shoes and stockings, he listened. All was still beyond the boxwood, for a moment.

Then, startlingly clear, a bell pealed from one of the academy porticoes; it pealed twice. It was the last bell, recalling the students from lunch-study; a boy not at his desk now was late. And tardiness from study period was unforgivable. No boy was supposed to stray out of earshot of the first bell that called him to class; that bell had rung, Gregory knew, a full six minutes before! He took a long run and leaped the hedge and scrambled up the lawn and through the laurel circle. Then he ran even harder. He was puffing hoarsely by the time he reached the southwest portico, which was nearest to his classroom. The old butler who had rung the brass handbell was shuffling slowly across the flagged portico toward the same door by which Gregory would have to enter the hall.

"Where you been, boy?" he asked kindly.

Gregory thought swiftly for a likely story. "I—I must have fallen asleep, the sun was so hot—I didn't hear the first bell!" he gasped, hoping that maybe he had heard amiss and by some miracle it was merely the first bell that old Yance had sounded.

The elderly man just muttered "Humph!" casually, but not as though he considered the tale incredible. Gregory wondered. A proctor, an upper classman, would be taking the attendance. Depending on who the proctor was, Gregory supposed he might get by with his story of falling asleep. If only Howard Carter were proctor— he was easygoing; or even Chuck Long, who had three younger brothers that were always getting into mischief and had perforce wheedled their senior into indulgence.

To Gregory's utter horror it was Keith proctoring! And the bigger boy glared at his young brother with sharp suspicion the moment Gregory shoved the big oak door in gently and slipped around it.

"So," Keith's voice snapped, actually much as his fa-

45

ther's might have under the same circumstance, "we have remarked your absence, Master Donlewis!"

Greg felt his stomach slip down a few inches. He made a sudden unconscious grab at his breeches as if he thought they had become loose at the waistline and would embarrass him. He walked up the aisle between the benches to his own place near the front. The eight boys who recited in Geometry with him all stared gravely, first at Gregory and then back at Keith. Gregory lost his self-confidence entirely. Keith wouldn't give a flea a chance, he knew; steeped in the honor of the family, Keith would crucify the corn broom if it failed in its kitchen duty! Greg stood beside his bench, tense, tight-mouthed.

"I said we remarked your absence!" Keith repeated, this time with sweet, tender, brotherly sarcasm that provoked a low titter from the boys seated farthest from his proctor's position at the master's desk.

Gregory gulped. "I . . . I . . . I . . ." after the third attempt to get started he blurted all of a piece, "fell asleep beneath the laurel bushes and missed the warning bell." It was said too awkwardly, he knew, hard-toned and blunt.

"You expect that's an excuse, enough of one to keep me from making report?" Keith demanded.

Gregory flushed—and knew he'd die reprimanded by old Dr. Bodewell himself before he begged mercy from his brother. "No, sir," he whispered formally, for a proctor received the same deferences as an instructor; then Greg tossed his head in true Donlewis defiance and added, "I expected no favors from you!"

"Well, unabashed and impudent too, eh?" Keith remarked, just as the door opened under the hand of Mr. Mensor, the mathematics master. "You will be seated, Master Donlewis," Keith finished properly.

Gregory slid into his place, feeling his face red-pepper-hot, and knowing, even though his eyes were cast down upon the worn walnut top of the double desk he shared with another boy, that Mr. Mensor eyed him thoroughly as he came up the aisle.

"I report Master Gregory Donlewis as tardy, sir," Keith let the accusation run smoothly from his mouth as though the name meant nothing at all to him.

"Was there not something about unabashed impudence too?" the master demanded, proving he had ears like a ferret.

Gregory noticed, with some faint satisfaction, that his brother reddened and ducked his head and picked up his copy of Ovid and his notebooks to hide the flush. What would Keith say?

When Keith spoke, it was sharp and cold. "A hint of impudence, sir!" Mr. Mensor might have been standing outside the door long enough to have heard the entire affair.

The master had a choice in the administration of discipline. He might demand that Gregory stay an hour or more after school or, if he so chose, he could send a formal report to the academy director, the headmaster, young Dr. Cecil Bodewell, the good old founder's grandson. Greg sweat out two theorems praying that Mr. Mensor would decide to keep him after school. Then Tad Boxbridge slipped him a note saying:

> Greg, quit hoping against it—
> he just wrote out the HS, I *saw!*

HS was their abbreviation for headmaster's slip, a memorandum to Master Cecil. Once written, it was always sent; and your name on such meant formal notification to your parent on the next report of standing. Gregory ground his back molars together and dug into Euclid. He had now quickly to forget the pallid suffering lad in Neever's shack. Religiously he put Bart out of mind for the remainder of the school day, in fact, until Keith pulled his horse up beside Patches on the way home, thus recalling the whole business swiftly to the younger boy.

"What were you doing that made you late?" Keith asked pleasantly enough. They were two miles along the way home and alone. The senior boy was sympathetic and Gregory knew that he was. But Greg was sore against the HS.

"I said." He bit the words out with finality.

"Oh no, you didn't say! I know better than to believe that hogwash about falling asleep in the sun, mister," Keith pursued.

"I said what I said," Gregory reiterated stubbornly.

"All right, be hound-jawed and pigheaded," Keith returned. "Tad told me old Mensor sent in an HS. You ought to be able to imagine what Father will say when Cecil Bodewell notates your report! Maybe if you tell me the truth, I can find something in the story that will get you off with Cecil; he's pretty lenient if you approach him intellectually," Keith continued with the senior student's sense of pride and privilege; patiently he held his horse at Patches's pace.

But Gregory, of course, could not tell part of the story without telling the rest, and he had promised Bart to say nothing to anyone. He rode doggedly at a slow trot with his lips rolled in and his eyes cast down upon the road, hoping to discourage Keith's curiosity by his unpleasantness. He looked rather guilty—of something—and Keith was thus goaded into questioning him all the way home. Once there, however, the older boy had chores to do and tough assignments in Greek and German; he soon forgot entirely about teasing Gregory.

Left in peace, Gregory applied himself assiduously to his duties in household, pharmacy, and surgery. He had

48

never been more diligent; he could hardly have been more helpful and enterprising if the dreaded note from Cecil Bodewell had been due to arrive at the surgeon's on the morrow. He got wood for all the woodboxes that needed replenishing; without being reminded, he hoed the new lettuce and spinach and asparagus in the kitchen garden and hauled in potatoes and turnips from the dugout. He even shined the marble slabs in the apothecary room and he was especially prompt and careful in the surgery. Between times he secreted discarded ends of bandage rolls, tearings of lint, a swipe of opium salve on a square of brown paper which his father had left from an afternoon dressing. Casually Gregory asked if the doctor didn't need to add to his supply of splints. There was a pile of good ash in the woodshed from which these were cut and Greg could make them. Yes, it was all right to make a few more if he had enough time from his other tasks. The surgeon stated no particular number, and Gregory felt free to fashion two extras to tuck under his saddlestrap the next morning.

At supper Greg managed to save two rolls and his potatoes. Later he offered to scrape the plates for Launa, and was thus able to roll up a paper containing carrot and ham scraps and three stalks of new asparagus. He managed to hide this package in his saddlebag along with the bandages and medicines. Afterward he filled a clean jar from the pharmacy with vinegar and sharpened his penknife on his father's honing stone, since he didn't want to be responsible for removing a scissors for an entire day. He went to bed after he had swept pharmacy, waiting room, and surgery, and stood by during the treatment of two patients. He was well satisfied with himself and with his preparations for Bart; he slept deep and happy, his arm about his dog, forgetful at last of the horrid HS.

V.

Trouble Snowballs

THE morrow proved bright again; no one questioned Gregory's whistling gaiety as he started out earlier than usual. Despite this precaution he was a very long time with Bart, too long. He had no watch and the time ran out like quicksilver from a broken barometer. First Gregory fed the hideaway lad; he noticed immediately that Bart was definitely fevered now; his cheeks and ears were flushed thick under his curious sick-pallor that still sat like a mask upon him. Gregory forced a full cup of vinegar water into him, after the practice of his surgeon father.

" 'Tis good in case you've any corruption, my father says, and also if you're not sure about the quality of creek water for drinking. My father doctored in the army during the War for Independence; he used vinegar all the time," Gregory explained.

Bart was so sick that he would probably have submitted to anything at all that might cure him! He drank the tangy water docilely. He was very tense and nervous; he jerked at the whir of a hawk rising outside somewhere, again at the sudden jawing of a bluejay irked by some impudent squirrel in the pines on the hilltop. Gregory washed and dressed the cut shoulder; it was an ugly wound. Greg dared not clean it thoroughly for fear it would open and bleed profusely; it was in a nasty place in the depression of the clavicle. Bart's arm was stiff and sore all the way to his wrist and swollen hard above the elbow; the lad could barely move his left fingers and only with great pain.

"Some surgeons say suppuration—the formation of pus like that which you have in your shoulder, and in your leg too—is good and promotes healing, but my father believes it is better if a wound heals by what he calls 'first intention,' almost immediately, without any pus." Gregory explained. He went on to describe how his father had spent four years in London studying at St. George's and St. Bartholomew's hospitals with the famous Hunters and Abernethy and others. He talked a lot for two reasons: to occupy Bart against his pain and to ease himself against the awful responsibility he was taking, doctoring the lad clandestinely thus against his better judgment.

Too much time had run out before Gregory reached the broken leg; he could only look at it cursorily and promise to come back at noon. He left Bart his square of chocolate from Launa, a clean handkerchief, and a fresh supply of creek water, which he doctored now with a measure of vinegar. Patches was stamping restlessly in the alder clump. Gregory threw leg over leather swiftly, struck the pony with the flat of his palm, and was soon clattering noisily across the wooden bridge with its rattly, loose planks. A liveried slaveboy opened the swinging iron gates that marked the academy entrance.

"Mornin', Massa Greg," he grinned pleasantly, for he knew all the students by name. "You're late!" he observed politely as he swung back on the bottom rung of the gate behind Patches's rear hoofs.

Greg pulled up on his reins and looked back, startled.

"Second double bell already rung!" the gateboy shouted to him through a cupped hand.

It had, indeed, and Greg's first class was Latin Literature with Cecil Bodewell himself. There wouldn't be any need for an HS. Gregory tiptoed down the hall after he had delivered Patches to a groom in the big half stable. Lem Butterwood was struggling with the opening lines of Book Two of the *Aeneid,* Greg could hear as he approached his classroom door, which stood slightly ajar. Well, Greg had the lesson, at least! He stepped into the classroom as quietly as possible and stood at his desk until Lem floundered quite hopelessly and was ordered to sit down.

Headmaster Bodewell looked down from his rostrum, leaning upon folded arms. He had gentle brown eyes under a mane of wavy blond hair, but Gregory did not look up to meet his gaze.

"You are really quite late, Master Donlewis. Why?" was all the headmaster said, in a very normal tone, yet Gregory felt as though an icy breeze had enveloped him.

"I—" He found his knees wobbly suddenly. He had not thought of any excuse. He stared at his boot toes and announced firmly, "I—have no excuse, sir."

Young Dr. Bodewell replied not at all but went on calmly with the lesson, gesturing Gregory into his seat with a slight flourish of his left hand. But that was not the end of the matter, Greg knew perfectly well! Anxious and thinking that he must certainly not risk going to see Bart at noon, chancing further tardiness—or still worse, the possibility of being caught beyond the hedge—Greg kept losing his place in the text. And he could not erase from his mind the hope on Bart's face as he had turned away out the wretched door that morning. . . .

The class plowed steadily through another hundred lines of Virgil; then Cecil digressed, as he could do so charmingly, with his own interpretations and descriptions of the material covered. He was a master teacher; the ancient world shone in the sunshine of his understanding. In this warmth Gregory basked for a while, at last forgetful until it was time to gather up books, pens, plumb line, and pencils and go into the court for a lecture on composition.

"Master Donlewis, you will report to my office before you go home this afternoon," the headmaster called as Gregory was about to leave the classroom.

Gregory bit back tears. He had never before been called to Headmaster Bodewell's office; it boded ill when one was thus summoned! The quiet command was enough to give the boy pause again for the rest of the morning in regard to the idea of risking departure at lunch time. But the drawn face of the boy in the cabin and the memory of the swollen leg which oozed pus so dangerously and was not splinted tormented him.

When it came to a decision, Gregory went. He couldn't stay away! He went just as soon as he dared and more furtively than he had the day before. Gregory had scarcely eaten any lunch but had stuffed his shirt and pockets with everything portable. He found Bart languid, unenthusiastic even about the food, though he ate it, knowing that the doctor's son had cajoled and stolen to comfort him.

"You must eat; you must keep up your strength," Gregory warned. "Oh, I do wish you'd let me bring my father to you; he wouldn't tell anyone, whomever you fear!"

"Wouldn't he now? As if ye know what I fear," Bart struggled to maintain a sheepish grin, like the half-bantering, half-defiant boy in the thicket, but he was much sicker, Gregory knew. His sharp, bold self-reliance was fading into miserable dependence on Gregory's service.

Gregory set himself to cleansing the broken leg. Though he had become accustomed to battling squeamishness and nausea and conquering his feelings in his father's surgery, still Greg was glad that he had eaten

53

scantily at lunch. He got much accumulated soil off. And once Bart fainted. Greg had to hang him off the poor cot with his head down and slap his cheeks to revive him. Fearfully, afterward, the doctor's son tried to set the bone ends together while Bart struggled not to scream. Gregory did not succeed at all, he knew; he could tell that the edges of bone were not fitted, Bart sank into another faint. Greg was afraid to go on. He revived Bart with a strong dilution of vinegar water which he held under his nose and then made him drink; afterward he bandaged the leg neatly as best he could, arranging the splints to keep it motionless. He made Bart as comfortable as possible with a piece of torn sheeting and a small pillow and old blanket he had managed to stuff into his saddlebag with everything else. Bart claimed his shoulder felt better under the smidgen of opium salve Gregory had pilfered, but the doctor's son did not like the beginning streaks of red along the upper portion of the sick lad's arm.

"Why don't you tell me what you've done and why you're afraid, why don't you?" Gregory begged again and again.

But Bart was adamant and folded his mouth tight. Greg promised to return the next morning, planning already to watch his time more carefully. He raced down to the creek, splashed through it from rock to rock, pulled on hose and boots swiftly. Yet to his horror the double bell rang out just as he leaped the hedge—he was late *again!* He had never imagined that trouble could chase him so. The rest of the day went leadenly, heavy under Greg's mental anguish, for Mr. Mensor again wrote out a blunt HS to young Dr. Bodewell.

Keith caught his young brother by the jacket collar in the hall at dismissal. "What the devil's the matter with you? I just heard you were late again this afternoon! Where are you going? What are you doing?"

"I'm not doing anything wrong, I'm not!" Gregory gasped, suddenly hoping it was true.

"If I didn't think Cecil would take adequate care of you, I'd tell Father myself," Keith muttered in Greg's ear, holding him tight by the shoulder with hard fingers that pinched wickedly.

"No!" Greg cried, agonized, "don't tell Father, don't!"

"So you've done nothing wrong, eh?" Keith asked shrewdly. "You've the distinction at least of being the first one of us, the first of nine Donlewises, to be called to the headmaster's office. Think you on that a bit!"

Gregory, both hurt and angry, scooted out of earshot to the back terrace to wait a few tense moments until the long halls cleared of merry, released boys. At last, no longer hearing voices in the hallways, Gregory opened the door back into the main corridor cautiously, found everything clear, and went up the huge walnut-paneled staircase painfully slowly, wondering what sort of office Cecil Bodewell had. It turned out to be an amazingly pleasant one, Greg found, after he had knocked and been admitted by a servant who ushered him to a tall walnut chair and then retired. Gregory had really expected to stand, perhaps to be kept waiting thus for some time, meditating on his sins! Instead he was able to sit comfortably in a room bright with sunshine that poured through the diamond-shaped panes of the casement windows. The heavy tapestry draperies that hung from the high windows were now pulled apart so that the sunlight came in grandly from the west. Two entire walls of the room were lined with books. A few tall, carved walnut chairs stood about, each with its bright red-velvet cushion upon its seat, and onto one of these Gregory eased his rear comfortably.

A big red medallion design in the thick carpet before a handsome hand-wrought walnut desk brightened the somber rich wood coloring. The scarlet cover on a large couch against the third wall gave another touch of color. Gregory studied a polished silver inkwell in the middle of the broad desk top and also a bronze statuette of Athena that stood as a paperweight on some letters at the right.

Presently the heavy oak door opened, admitting the young director. Gregory jumped to his feet as the headmaster grunted, "Ah, huh!" recognizing him.

"Good . . . after . . . noon . . . sir." Gregory gulped painfully.

"What's good about it—for you?" Cecil demanded with a straight face.

"I . . . don't . . . really . . . know . . . sir," Gregory answered with care. He had been taught to reply to his elders immediately, something polite.

The young headmaster went behind his desk and set his books and papers from his last class upon it. He sat down, settling himself comfortably in the squarish walnut armchair that had an even thicker velvet cushion than its companion straight chairs. Gregory came automatically to stand opposite at the center of the desk, for thus you reported to any master who summoned you, in class or out.

"Suppose you tell me, boy, exactly why you have been tardy. I received another memorandum indicating that you repeated the offense again this after-lunch. Surely you are far from dull, so that you must be aware that you are breaking school regulations. Why? Exactly why are you?" Dr. Bodewell asked.

"I'm truly sorry to have been late, but I cannot say why," Greg all but clenched his teeth after he got out what must have seemed a rather inconsistent statement to the headmaster.

"Indeed," Cecil received it coolly. "I should ask whether you know that I may exercise an arbitrary judgment in punishing you for the first offense and again for the next two, but should you be tardy again, the disciplinary action becomes a matter of academy policy. Do you know what I mean?"

Gregory's mouth dried at this and he licked his upper lip anxiously. "Yes, sir," he admitted.

"Exactly what do you understand?" the headmaster pursued.

Gregory swallowed with difficulty. "That I should have to be whipped," he whispered, "at assembly, Friday afternoon." He had seen such a thing once and it had been solemn, unforgettable, bitterly impressive.

"Just so," Bodewell acknowledged. "I personally am somewhat undetermined about whippings and I cannot really see why they should ever be necessary among young gentlemen of the background and intelligence of our students here. However, custom is often stronger than common sense and usually stronger than individual personal opinion, and one is caught up on all sides in a mesh of custom! Also when a boy of your caliber, Gregory Donlewis, turns stubborn obviously, I am inclined to feel that the old rule is righteous! Has it occurred to you, boy, that there might reasonably be an acceptance of your offenses, *if* you explained the nature of their cause?"

"I have nothing to say, sir," Gregory blurted hastily before Cecil's charm had any chance to overcome his better judgment; after all, he had promised Bart faithfully to hold his peace.

"I see. Then it appears, under the circumstances, that I must interrogate you further. It is quite inconceivable to me that the warning bell after lunch study could be missed by anyone within the normal environs of the academy. Since you have been late twice after lunch, I would inquire as to whether you know now and knew earlier that it is forbidden to trespass beyond the privet hedge?" Bodewell leaned across his desk; his gentle eyes searched the boy's face.

Gregory could not falsify under such solemn heart-to-heart earnestness, though he were beaten twice. He said without a second's hesitation, "I know the rule about not passing the hedge, sir, and I have always known it."

"And were you out of hearing of the bell? Beyond the hedge?"

An affirmative answer doubled the after-lunch offenses, of course, and made Gregory immediately subject to the discipline beyond the third error, if Bodewell chose to regard the matter thus. Gregory wet his lips again and shifted on his feet uncomfortably. "I—" he began wretchedly and his tongue felt unconscionably thick. "I was beyond the hedge, Dr. Bodewell," he got out finally in a tight whisper.

"So." The small word had a horrid finality as though Cecil were closing the book before he threw it at the culprit before him. "You may go. I will consider the case."

Gregory wanted desperately to protest. He would have welcomed immediate punishment, no matter how drastic, welcomed getting it over whatever it was to be. To be hung up by them both—Keith threatening to tell their father; Cecil thinking heaven knew what! He went out heavily and closed the huge door gingerly behind him, remembering to bite out a compulsive "Good afternoon, sir," the last second.

VI.

Gregory Pays the Price

IT was good that Patches was willing to dogtrot this pleasant afternoon, because Greg rode all the way home without any control on the reins. He was wrestling with the fact that he must not risk tardiness again and also with the other knowledge that if he did not take food, water, and comfort to the poor boy in the ramshackle cabin, Bart might die. It was a pretty problem. No wonder that at home Greg spilled charcoal in the pharmacy, soiling a just-scrubbed floor, broke two eggs from a basket he was fetching from the barn, and irked his father into boxing his ears in the surgery because he brought the wrong instruments twice and dropped two ligatures.

"Get to bed!" the surgeon roared in exasperation at nine o'clock. "You're no blasted good to anyone tonight."

Keith, coming out of the kitchen, encountered his brother in the passage; Greg's eartips showed red through his black curls and he was twisting at his queuestring with nervous fingers. "Conscience troubling you?" the older boy asked sweetly, running an index finger flat under Greg's nose and forcing him to flip his head back.

Gregory really wanted to plead with him against the teasing, to remind him that he had promised not to tell —but then he remembered worriedly that Keith hadn't promised anything since that day's more pronounced developments. He growled an angry denial. "No, it's *not* troubling me!"

"Utterly innocent, eh, butterfingers? I suppose that's why you've churned up such a mess in surgery tonight

59

that the old man threw you out loud enough to be heard in Henrico County, heh?" Keith taunted.

Gregory ran into his bedroom and slammed the door. He stripped quickly, got into his nightshirt and crawled under the covers, comforted by the pleasant warmth of Tawny against his stomach.

He had to get up early to get his morning tasks done and raid the pantry for leftovers before Launa came into the main house from her cabin. He was lucky enough to find some cold sweet potatoes and he took two, along with a morsel of cabbage, a square of bacon, some scraps of cold ham, leftover rolls and bits of crumbled corn pone Launa was probably saving for the chicks. Being cautious, Greg didn't take all of anything; and he managed to pour half his own milk for his gruel into a small bottle he had hidden in his pocket.

All the way to Stony Creek Crossing, Gregory urged Patches to outdo himself, and later he cut across country through the Cremar plantation, something he was forbidden to do but the trick saved him two miles. The pony grumbled a little, snorting and tossing his head, but it was coolish that early and he obliged by trotting lively most of the way. Greg took Patches up the hill to Neever's shack this time instead of leaving him in the alder clump; it was better to have him tied comfortably close to the cabin where he'd be ready for a quick dash to the academy.

At Greg's first scratching signals no reply came from within, but after a second series Bart finally called out hoarsely, "Gregory?"

The poor boy was much sicker. He couldn't eat the bacon and ham, though he wolfed the bread and pone soaked in the fresh milk. He was glassy-eyed, lackluster, wasted with fever; his lips were cracked, his tongue badly coated. The cabin reeked with a fetid, nasty smell.

60

The bandage on the leg was already putrid with ooze, the left arm worse streaked. Gregory panicked a little when Bart tried to shift his position slightly and fainted dead away. Luckily Greg had remembered to tuck a vial of hartshorn in his saddlebag; he ran to get it.

"Scare ye?" Bart whispered as he choked a bit coming to upon the acrid essence. "I kind of go off like that every couple hours, guess because I'm not sleepin' right, worryin' like I am. My leg feels a lot better."

"It's not better at all," Gregory interrupted bluntly. " 'Tis evil that it feels better." The boy did not understand him, perhaps fortunately, because the surgeon's son was thinking of the hideous possibility of gangrene and the usual feeling of well-being that preceded its fatal onslaught. "Please let me tell my father to come to you, please!"

But Bart would not hear of it and Gregory was too proud to tell of his trouble at school. Leaving what remained of the food and also the vial of hartshorn, Gregory thought that he was getting away in plenty of time, but he had underestimated the length of the fainting spell. The other horses and ponies were all neatly stalled when Greg turned Patches over to the stableboy. As Yance, the butler, opened the front door for him, Gregory was immediately faced with his delinquency. "Massa Cecil wants you to report to him upstairs, Massa Greg Donlewis, instead of to your study chair in the lib'ry," the old man informed him.

"Yance, how late am I?" Gregory demanded anxiously.

He shrugged, "Ten-twelve minutes maybe . . ."

"Odysseus!" Greg exclaimed, and turned grimly toward the staircase.

The headmaster had no early class on Fridays. He was behind his big desk and he looked up immediately and gravely at Greg's entrance. "Have you decided to present an excuse?" he asked directly and without banter. He knew Gregory well; he knew all the Donlewises. They were a proud, stubborn lot. Cecil could scarcely imagine Gregory Donlewis adamant Thursday and amenable Friday and, of course, he was right. The boy stood sternly silent. "Wait!" Bodewell rose, went out, closed the great door carefully behind him.

Gregory stood just where he was. He didn't even turn around. He stared across the desk top and out between the bottom mullions of the big casement window at the sprays of white blossoms on the locust tree outside; it was a tall tree and the sweet perfume of its blossoms permeated the room through the left window panel, which stood ajar. Even when the door opened in again at his back, Gregory did not turn around. He expected the headmaster to come back to his desk. A hand upon his right shoulder, therefore, startled him badly. He half jumped and looked around quickly into Keith's hazel eyes.

"Greg, let's get down to business on this. Where the devil have you been? What's making you late?"

"I can't tell, I can't! Don't you understand that I can't because it concerns someone else? I've promised and believe me, 'tis no light thing. I've got into it and given my word and I—I don't know what to do but I can't tell!" His face worked as he tried not to let his worry and fear and chagrin overcome him.

"I'm sorry I bullied you," Keith was newly sympathetic. "I guess I thought it was a joke or just carelessness at first, but Greg, Cecil sent me to talk to you because he—well, he doesn't want to beat you! For heaven's sake, don't you understand? You've already got a mess of stuff to go on your report to Father: late four times, admittedly out of bounds twice, stubbornness, refusal to explain your behavior. None of us has ever been in this kind of trouble; can't you just see the old man? Maybe the whole thing's not so bad if you would only tell us?" Keith pleaded. "At least, tell me!"

Greg thought sharply of how he had pleaded just so with the strange lad in the miserable shack. "I *can't* tell," he cried.

"Well, you needn't scream at me; that's not helping anything," Keith set a foot carelessly upon one of the walnut chair seats and then dropped it off again quickly, considering the red cushion. "You recognize that you'll be hauled up this aft' and flogged before everybody, don't you? The only one who can get you out of it is Cecil. . . ."

Gregory winced under the cold tremor that ran up his spine; he set his teeth and twisted his fingers together miserably. "Keith, you won't tell Father, will you?" he begged tight-throated.

His brother merely sniffed. "I won't have to—it'll all be in black and white, plain to be read!"

"I know that, but he'll not get the report until the end of the month, at least. Don't tell before, Keith, *please.* He'll—he'll——"

"He'll kick you out of the surgery, I'll tell you that much!" Keith voiced what Gregory knew full well but hadn't brought himself to put into words. The older lad felt genuinely sorry for Gregory: the boy had always been exemplary; he liked fun, yes, but that he could be in anything seriously evil, Keith, like the headmaster, could not conceive. "All right, I'll not tell Father—not now anyhow."

"Promise?" Gregory whispered, crossing his heart feebly.

Keith smiled but repeated the "hope to die" rhyme softly complete with the binding gesture.

"Keith? You're certain I'll be . . . beat . . ." Gregory asked then, very low.

"Yes, 'tis the school ruling; even if you tell Cecil everything, you may be, depending on how he interprets the entire affair. Shall you tell now?"

"No."

For a long moment silence thickened between them. Gregory knew how he would be punished; he asked finally just to fend against it, "I'll be caned? . . . by Donovan?" He murmured the questions. "How many stripes, d'ye think?"

Donovan was their Irish riding master who handled games, taught horsemanship and natural science, kept the boys physically fit, and took care of all outdoor matters —and who also administered any physical discipline.

"That's for Cecil to decide. I would think anything from six to fifteen, and you'd not stand fifteen at one time," Keith warned.

Gregory could hardly swallow.

Keith made his final plea. "Better you tell one of us everything there is to tell, boy, now!"

But the younger brother shook his head stubbornly. The door opened softly again to admit the young headmaster, who looked to Keith with a swift "Well?"

"He has told me nothing, sir," the older Donlewis was forced to report.

"I'm sorry," Cecil said with finality. "You will stay with him."

Greg's face flamed with shame. So he was to be guarded like a prisoner; he could not get back to Bart at lunch time, and the lad needed him. He turned reluctantly out the door of the director's office with Keith at his shoulder.

"If at any time during the day Master Gregory regrets his decision toward silence, my office door will be open," young Dr. Bodewell said with kindly warmth as the lads stepped into the hallway.

Gregory sat in the library with Keith at his elbow, went monitored to his classes, ate his lunch, studied on the terrace with the bigger boy beside him. Gregory kept his mouth set sullen. The brothers spoke less than a dozen words all the while and usually these were Keith's brief petitions for confession and Greg's reiterated "I can't tell!"

General assembly for the entire academy was at two-thirty. Just before all the boys went to put up their books at their desks in the rooms to which they were permanently assigned as a base, Keith tightened his hands on his junior's shoulders. "Hear me," he muttered behind a convenient pillar on the portico. "You've still five minutes. Go up and talk to Cecil . . ."

Gregory made no answer. Keith's fingers pinched. "No Donlewis has been publicly disciplined before, think you firm on the disgrace," Keith said and then sneered, "Don't augment it by howling, confound you!" He released his hands and turned away from Gregory angrily. Since he had remained stubborn, Gregory would never run from his punishment, Keith knew. With his jaw set against revealing a sympathy which might render Greg less stanch at the crucial moment, Keith strode off to join his own form at the rear of the assembly hall.

Gregory went into the large, dark-paneled room and sat properly at his regular place on the aisle in the second row, right. His fellows filed in one by one soberly; many eyed him curiously, puzzled, even sympathetic, but none spoke. Mr. Rouart, the European-languages instructor, had the program for the day and was already up on the rostrum organizing the lads who would participate. It proved to be a nice program: a dramatic recitation of Schiller's *Das Lied von der Glocke,* some French and

Spanish songs—but Gregory could not appreciate it! He cast furtive glances at young Dr. Bodewell, who sat calmly right front, and also at Mr. Donovan, who was decidedly present front left. Across the speaker's stand before Cecil lay the standard instrument of discipline, the leather-handled birch cane which was never laid there unless it was to be employed. Gregory could not doubt that it was there solely for his benefit.

After Mr. Rouart's class had been duly applauded and returned to their places, the headmaster arose and made his announcements for the week. Then Bodewell paused, shifted some papers in his hand and next made the usual honor awards for the week to four boys; one was Keith, who went forward proudly and received the purple bookmark that was passed from student to student for the best Greek translation of the week. Not two minutes later the name Donlewis rang through the hall again, this time unvarnished, without honor: "Master Gregory Donlewis will step forward for discipline!"

Tension tugged along the junior-form rows immediately. There had been the usual rumors, confirmed somewhat by the appearance of the cane on the stand; the final assurance touched the younger boys into a sharp pity that was breathed softly from row to row. If no one would say any more—if it could just be got over quickly, Gregory thought—— He pushed himself to stand up, though his whole body felt lead-heavy and his face flared scarlet. He thanked heaven he sat so far front and had not the whole length of hall to traverse. Cecil was saying more: "For repeated unexcused tardiness and the admission that he was absent without leave during the school day on several occasions, the named Master Gregory Donlewis is ordered ten strokes with the usual disciplinary instrument applied in the usual manner." If the Donlewises had not been so proud and so brilliant, so well reputed and so genuinely liked, there would have been tittering at Cecil's rather delicately worded announcement, but the entire assemblage remained immeasurably, embarrassingly, still.

Mr. Donovan crossed swiftly before Gregory and took up the cane. A second later he reached for the boy, who stood now with blazing cheeks front center before the low rail that separated the performance platform from the seating section of the assembly hall. Mr. Donovan never minced matters; he thrust Gregory down upon his knees across the rail in a single swift movement. Immediately the cane came down stingingly upon Greg's behind. The first blow was shocking and sharp indeed; Gregory ground his teeth together hard. As the cane kept descending, the pain worsened, becoming hot and agonizing until the boy felt a scream gathering in his throat, pushing toward his set lips. He grasped at the platform edge beyond the railing with both hands and fought against crying out; he winked hot tears from his eyes. Gregory lost count as succeeding blows re-emphasized the hurt of earlier ones, but Mr. Donovan counted accurately and stalked off with the cane after ten without a word and without lifting the miserable culprit from the rail. Gregory wanted to remain as he was with his head down while the entire assemblage filed out, but he dared not. He swept his face across his jacket sleeve stealthily, pushed up from the rail, stood quite erect and turned at last toward the sea of faces that stared at him anxiously. He managed to walk the six steps to his seat steadily enough; he sat down, somewhat painfully in very truth! A moment later the classes, at signal, began to file out. No one spoke to Gregory even after everyone reached the passages. Gregory walked past the arch that marked the main entrance to the library; he was suddenly snatched at from the right side and pulled into a small sitting room. Keith

67

shut the door carefully behind them. Gregory looked up into his face.

"I was proud of you," Keith whispered. "Ten's a lot all at once!"

"Proud of me?" Gregory protested. "I'd never imagined I could be so ashamed, so terribly ashamed!" The hot tears he had held back so bravely came pouring suddenly; he bent his head and butted his face into Keith's corduroy jacket and sobbed.

Keith put a kind arm across his shoulders and let him cry. A bit later he gave the younger boy his handkerchief. "Think you can ride home all right, eh?" he asked finally with a tinge of facetiousness. "Better lengthen your stirrups and stand saddle—it'll feel worse before it feels better, y'know."

"I'll be all right," Gregory muttered; then, remembering, he tugged at Keith's arm. "Don't tell Father—you promised!"

"I know," Keith returned a little sourly. "Here, let me dust you up a bit," he wet his kerchief with his lips and wiped away the tearstains from Greg's face and straightened the younger boy's collar and wrist pleats of white lawn. "Go along now and keep your head up. You've paid, you've been punished; the shame's over until you err again. Always remember that about punishment—sometimes it's good because it gets the whole thing over; it pays your debt to society!"

Gregory tossed his head up; he hadn't thought of the whole thing that way. He was back on equal terms with his classmates and they'd no right to whisper about him, if they did, he could take care of it. "Thanks," he murmured to his brother and went out proud again. He even had the courage to say "Good afternoon, sir" firmly to young Dr. Bodewell, whom he passed crossing the terrace.

VII.

A Vain Sacrifice

THE ride home was far from pleasant. Even a slow trot put rather painful emphasis upon the insulted portion of Greg's anatomy. He was grinding his teeth from pain by the time he pulled Patches up in their barn, and he discovered to his complete distress, upon dismounting, that walking was hardly any easier. Indeed it took poor Gregory exasperatingly long to get his normal tasks accomplished. The doctor would surely have noticed the boy's slow, pained movements, had he not been unusually preoccupied with a blacksmith's apprentice who had slipped in the forge and run his arm against a hot tongs.

At suppertime Keith watched his brother carefully and noted that Greg hid his discomfort well. Luckily, too, Friday was bread-making night. Launa, one of her older daughters, and Mistress Donlewis were all three up to their elbows in flour and dough, kneading and shaping immediately after supper. No one paid Gregory much heed.

After the blacksmith's lad had been treated and had gone off to his master's house, the surgeon ate a late supper from a tray in the study. Later Gregory, coming to pick up the tray, was ordered to tote wood into the hospital room, where there were two patients. The evening had a chilly cast and one of the patients was fevered and had to be guarded against cold. Poor Greg ached wretchedly under the burden of the cut logs, for it was a fairly long trip to the big woodpile. He had to go through the waiting room to get into the hospital, too.

His father stood there talking to a prospective patient. As the surgeon quietly reassured the man about a coming operation, Gregory went back and forth several times. His father had the chance to remark him carefully.

As soon as his client went out, Stephen Donlewis arrested his son with a kindly interest. "Did you fall today?"

Gregory turned to him, startled, and felt his color rise. "No, sir," he replied quickly.

"Stiff neck? Backache?" the doctor wondered.

"Oh no, sir, I'm not ill!" he denied trouble with the mechanical swiftness that always gave him away.

"Then what the devil's the matter with you?" the doctor roared, his suspicion touched off. "You're stooped and halting like an old man!"

Gregory marched on with his armload of wood, pulling an agonized breath tight through his nose and hoping to get out of sight and sound of his father. He deposited the logs in the woodbox beside the hospital fireplace and spent a couple of unnecessary moments rearranging the ones already placed for lighting. Carefully, with the flint gun, he struck fire to the shavings. Perhaps if he took long enough, the doctor would go into his study and become too occupied to remember him? Despite all his care to prolong his time in the hospital room, Gregory found his father still leaning against the surgery railing when he finally emerged.

"Why are you walking so oddly?" the surgeon demanded.

"I—I hadn't noticed anything," Gregory muttered, sure that his telltale face had turned all colors of the rainbow. His father reached out a fine hand and upturned the boy's chin, demanding his eyes.

"You haven't fallen and you're not sick; have you perchance been whipped at school?" he hazarded.

Gregory's face burned and he tried to drop his head against the doctor's firm grasp.

"Well?" This time his father's reiterated softness of tone was a definite sign of displeasure.

"Caned . . . yes, sir," Gregory admitted at last.

"Go lie on my couch and let me have a look. By Jupiter, they must have done it well to have you hurting still," the doctor observed.

Gregory had a sudden wonderful thought that perhaps his father would be outraged, and righteously so, at ten stripes! But immediately remembering his pledge of secrecy to Bart, the boy realized that this could hardly happen if the doctor were told no more than Dr. Bodewell and Keith. The inevitable question came as Gregory unloosed his breeches and rolled them down, somewhat abashed.

"Why were you whipped, boy?"

"Be—because I was tardy . . . and . . . and . . ." He might as well get it out because his father would worm it from him soon enough, he knew. "And also I was out from the school grounds during session."

"So." The doctor said the small word as sourly as Cecil Bodewell had. He scanned the bruised bottom with a professional eye. He went into the pharmacy room and got the limewater and a cloth and presently laid the latter, well soaked, upon the humiliated derrière. But at the same time he demanded, hard, why his son had been tardy and out of bounds. "To my knowledge you have the distinction of being the first of my sons to be thus decorated at Bodewell's Academy," he added sourly, nodding in the direction of the damage.

"I can't say why, sir," Gregory mumbled with his mouth almost buried in the couch cover.

"What?"

"I can't tell—I couldn't tell Dr. Bodewell and—that's why he had to have me beat——"

The next few moments Gregory never afterward cared to recall. His father became increasingly angry as Greg remained firmly silent. Finally the surgeon jerked the boy off the couch by an ear.

"I didn't do wrong, I swear, I *swear!*" Gregory protested then, and tears scalded his already hot cheeks.

"An interesting statement when I know blasted well that Cecil Bodewell would rather beat his grandmother than one of his beloved students!" the doctor retorted bitterly. "You admit that you broke the school regulations sneakily and repeatedly, yet you swear you have done naught reprehensible. Whom are you defending then and why? Tell me immediately!" His fingers were not light upon the ear; his face was as implacable as Greg had ever seen it.

The poor boy shook in his shoes. "I want to tell—I do truly—but I promised not, you see, and I can't! 'Tis important to someone that I hold my peace," he cried.

"I do not see! And I want no boy about who cannot be open and aboveboard in everything; before the Almighty, Gregory, I am your father!" the doctor reminded him. Then he said, "Go to your room and report no more as apprentice here!"

Thus it happened, what Greg had most dreaded. His father had only once in his lifetime taken back a dismissed student and never an apprentice! Gregory felt sick all over. He limped from the surgery, rubbing his tingly ear, miserable to wretchedness, hitching up his breeches over the limewater pad that was scarcely any comfort now. He heard his father send Tullah to find Keith. The older boy had no chance to keep his promise to his younger brother, for the doctor demanded bluntly, "What do you know of Gregory's being flogged at school for disobedience?"

Keith told what he knew, since he'd no choice, and added that he could only regret that he knew so little.

"Tullah," Greg heard his father call, "go close the door to Gregory's room." He was shut thus into a chrysalis of private shame.

Dr. Donlewis looked in upon his son before he retired at midnight. Gregory had crawled between his sheets in just the limewater pad and his skin. His pup lay sprawled across his shoulders. Raising a woolly head, Tawny grumbled, still puppylike, at the surgeon's intrusion. The doctor smeared some opium salve on the bruised stripes. At the first touch of his hand Gregory sighed; then he started awake. Seeing his father in the light of the lantern he had set upon the commode, Greg swallowed his anguish bravely as the surgeon's firm fingers rubbed the ointment where it would do the most good. The doctor did not speak; Gregory knew that he would probably refuse him speech until the whole matter was cleared up. The boy gulped genuine hurt in full measure, for he worshiped his father and could not easily support his displeasure. He murmured a "thank you" for the soothing treatment, but if the doctor heard, he gave no indication of it.

Greg was restless all night, tossing against the dog and making him grunt. Whenever the boy woke from thick but troubled sleep, he was confronted with the memory of the shockheaded lad in the run-down cabin. Should he leave Bart alone now? Of course he had already got into so much trouble tending him that he could hardly make matters worse. To abandon the lad when he had stood so stoutly by his promise of silence seemed an untoward course, since it would surely serve Bart ill and could do nothing to clear up the mystery of Greg's own

73

offenses. The boy's final decision was to try again to get the runaway to accept the services of the doctor; if Gregory could bring his father to the cabin to see Bart, everything would be explained! Determined upon a last attempt in that direction, Greg went deeply to sleep just before dawn. He woke by himself a bit past the regular time.

Without chores to do in and about the surgery, Gregory sat awhile listlessly upon his bedside; not even the dog's tugging at his breeches' knee buckle for attention roused him. He ached rather badly in places and all movement was difficult. Eventually he forced himself to walk about, bend over, sit down and stand up, considering that he must do such things all day long. By breakfast time he was no longer quite so stiff and sore. He had saved nothing from supper and he was able to pocket only a little new bread and his porridge milk in the bottle he had brought back the previous day. He set out early for school, knowing that he could not trot Patches very comfortably and quite certain that he must not again be tardy!

Bart was almost comatose, Gregory found; he revived slowly and painfully. His left arm was swollen and streaked and his right leg immobile and numb. Gregory was terribly worried and said so.

"Please let me tell my father to come! I—er—I have got into a bit of trouble at school because of coming here and I don't think I dare come again at noon," Greg explained.

Bart's blue eyes were dulled now with his sickness and very troubled. "I'm sorry," he offered immediately. "I didn' want fer yuh ter git in no trouble!"

" 'Tis all right," Gregory reassured him gallantly, remembering Keith's statement that he had paid for his past sins, "that is, it's all right if I just don't get into

74

any more." It wasn't all right, really, not with his father, and his father's good opinion was Gregory's life!

"I'll think, this mornin'," Bart promised, after he had drunk the milk and eaten the bread. "If yuh could come back fer jest a few minutes at noon, mebbe I'll have it worked out, what ter do about yer paw; I reckon I cain't stay here much longer by m'sel'; I gotta be beholdin' somewheres." He fumbled with his shirt pocket and plucked out his little canvas sack. "Greg, I ain't got nothin' in the world of value 'ceptin' this. I want yuh ter take it," he whispered in his hoarse voice. "I think 'tis a good piece and I'm wantin' to give it ye for all ye've done fer me!" He thrust out the little bag feebly. "Open it, go on, pull the threads out."

Gregory shook his head. "No, I'll not take anything, Bart, for I've no need. You keep what is yours."

"Open it fer me, then, I want ter look at it," Bart said and added, "it was my mother's . . ."

Greg picked at the string and loosened a loop to bite into; then the homemade sack opened and revealed a pinlike piece of jewelry; it was shaped like a butterfly wing, the left one. It was of filigreed gold inlaid with blue-and-white enamel and set with pretty stones, red, green, and blue; the letter *J* was laid in the middle in seed pearls.

"Ain't it right pretty?" Bart asked. "It was my mother's," he repeated. "Now you jest take it. . . ."

"No indeed, I'll not," Gregory folded it back in the dirty linen and knotted the ends of thread to keep it safe. He tucked the whole back into Bart's pocket. "Please, Bart, if you really want to do something to—to thank me," he suggested softly, "then let me bring my father here to help you."

"I'll think about it, I promise; cain't you come back fer a minute at noon?" Bart pleaded.

"I shouldn't, but I'll try, and I'll bring you something better to eat," Greg pledged.

Accordingly, he fidgeted the morning classes through, unable to get Bart out of mind. He gulped his lunch, saving half of each item of it, half of his sweet potatoes and chicken, half his cabbage and rolls, and then nearly all of his piece of gingercake. He found the southeast lawn almost deserted, so he got over the hedge quickly and successfully. As usual, he left shoes and stockings at the creekside and went barefoot to the cabin. Coming in close from the cluster of pines on the hilltop, Greg noticed the cabin door swinging in, and he hadn't remembered leaving it so. He came on swifter. Looking through the doorway, he saw immediately that the shack was empty. Only the rotting pile of green apples and the dirty square of blanket on which the hurt boy had first bedded were there. Bart was gone! And with him Gregory's canteen, his bottle with the milk ration, the small pillow he had supplied, the torn sheets, the blanket——

Staring, nonplused, the boy soon panicked. He searched for some clue to the disappearance, but it was complete and unexplainable. No hoofmarks showed outside either, no scuffling of the ground or any sign of a struggle. The strange boy was just gone, and yet that morning early he had barely been able to lift his flushed head from the cot, he had had no motion in his left fingers. . . .

Running back down the hill from the place as though it were evil now and he could not bear being within its environs, Gregory whipped himself into a veritable frenzy of worry. By the time he waded into the creek and began his leaping course from stone to stone across it, he was weighted down under a sense of personal calamity. By the time he struggled, out of breath, up the smooth, sloping lawn to the academy buildings, he was near hysteria. Why, everything had been in vain, his playing the good

Samaritan, his taking the beating, everything! And any alibi he might have had—to his father, to Cecil, to anyone—had fallen about his ears. As it was now, who would believe there had ever been a boy like Bart? Bitterly Greg remembered the offering of the pin and knew that the piece of jewelry would have been some tangible evidence if he had only accepted it. Desperate, the boy could think only of his father; he wanted to talk to him, to blurt out the whole story, for the doctor never got ruffled—he would know what to do if there were something possible to do!

VIII.

A Crisis Approaches

A TRIBUTE to Cecil Bodewell as headmaster of the distinguished school his grandfather had started, was the fact that a scholar in serious trouble went to him as naturally and freely as he breathed. Perhaps he was not even surprised when Gregory's nervous rat-tat on his office door was followed by the quick scuttle of the half-gasping lad to a position of semicourtesy before the big walnut desk.

"Sir, I must go home, I simply must! Please let me! I have to talk to my father right away!" Gregory cried.

Dr. Bodewell was cool and direct; he didn't even suggest finding Keith. He had no doubt that Gregory would go directly to his father, as he said; so the headmaster gave him leave immediately, without further question, guarantee, or penalty. Halfway home Gregory realized how he had been trusted thus, before the afternoon session had even begun, set free to take himself off. During the long ride the boy sobbed a little, dryly, and finally calmed enough to organize his thoughts. But as he came into the outskirts of Fairville, past mill and tavern, he began to panic again. Suppose his father wouldn't believe his story? He was thoroughly stirred up by the time he flung his reins over the hitching post for patients' horses just outside the waiting-room door. He ran up the two stone steps to the door, praying fervently that the surgeon was not busy.

"Your father's in hospital," Tullah, who was sweeping the waiting-room floor, advised. Leaning on his broom a moment and pushing his fingers through his whitening curls, the colored man observed, "Steamed up today, and kinda early, Massa Greg!"

Dr. Donlewis heard this remark and looked out of the open hospital-room door. Seeing Gregory nervously cupping his elbows in his hands, the surgeon came into the waiting room too, wiping wet hands on his canvas apron. "Home already, son?" he asked.

"Sir, I—I have to tell you something," Gregory began.

His father nodded, dropped upon a chair and kicked out a stool for the boy. The whole story came out more easily than Gregory had thought it could, more easily and more logically. The doctor listened without interrupting, a hand pressed tight against his bad knee.

"I don't know what to do now or how I can ever tell Dr. Bodewell what really happened; I've naught to prove the boy was there. . . ." Gregory concluded; he kept running his forefinger under his nose as though he feared he would sneeze.

His father handed him a pocket handkerchief almost absently and the boy stopped the nervous gesture. "Well, I shall take care of whatever needs to be done later," the doctor said. "I must admit that there are several things that should be done. Pull yourself together, boy. Perhaps you'll feel better to be about something; there's a new patient in the hospital room who needs to be bathed. I had started on him; you go now and get the fellow decently clean!" he ordered and untied the big apron and tossed it to his son.

Gregory was afraid to smile; was he being taken back? Did his father hold him blameless or at least properly penitent for what he had done? He dared not ask. He knotted the neckband so the apron would not hang below his knees; then he put it on carefully and went into the hospital. The two preceding patients had been discharged that morning. The only occupied bed was near the fireplace. Gregory noted the basin of hot water and the towels his father had been using; then he looked down at the patient, who was naked beneath the sheet and whose pile of filthy clothing lay ominously near the hearth at the foot of the cot.

"Bart!" Gregory screamed, for it was he, looking a little odd with his face already three shades cleaner, though yet drawn with his illness.

The strange lad turned his head painfully against the ache of his shoulder, which the doctor had already washed carefully and dressed with a fold of clean, dry linen. Weakly Bart proffered his right hand, and Gregory laid his own in it.

"Ye told yer father anyhow?" Bart stated in his gasping, hoarse voice; he tried hard to smile.

"No!" Gregory exclaimed.

"Well, 'twas he brought me here and he's done treated me mighty fine so far and not axed nothin'," Bart continued. "He gimme some broth and a pill to make me sleepy and this nice clean bed. . . ."

"I have to get *you* clean," Gregory told him matter-of-factly. He set about the task thoroughly, as he had been

79

taught, folding back only part of the sheeting at a time so the patient would not be cold or have his feelings outraged. Bart suffered his ministration patiently; he lay holding onto the cotside with his good hand and he never murmured even when Gregory worked on the broken leg. The doctor had taken off the splints and laid the wound open. Gregory washed it thoroughly and gently but with a fairly strong vinegar-water solution. He had nearly finished when Bart whispered to him urgently.

"Greg, I'm gonna be—sick——" and he was, horribly, in the basin Greg held for him.

The doctor came in just then. "Go heat another cup of broth warm enough so he can comfortably drink it," he ordered Gregory.

"I better not have no more, suh," Bart suggested. "I jes' keep on tossin' it up."

Dr. Donlewis sat down on the cot alongside Bart's and shook his head. "It's not the broth, lad; you must get fluid in you, lots of it, whether you are sick or not. 'Tis the opium you're nauseating on and I'm sorry, because it would have helped the pain a little. I've had other folk like you, boy—what did you say your name was?"

"I didn' say, suh," Bart admitted sheepishly, "but 'tis Bart."

"Well, Bart, some people cannot tolerate opium and since you have now vomited up three separate doses, I more than suspect that you are one of those people," the surgeon explained. "I have to fix your shoulder and your leg; it won't be very pleasant," he warned.

The raggy yellow head nodded against the white pillow. While Gregory went for the broth, the doctor attached canvas strips to both of Bart's ankles; from these, heavy flat stones were suspended to pull the lad's legs taut. When Greg hand-fed Bart the broth, he noticed that the poor boy's cheeks were wet. But Bart made neither outcry nor protest. Afterward the doctor took away his pillow and left him lying perfectly flat during the lengthening afternoon.

Several hours later the surgeon called his son from some scouring he was doing in the apothecary room and ordered preparations for the setting of Bart's leg. The strange boy had been lying quiet against the aching pull of the heavy stones. He seemed heavily flushed with fever and probably did not recognize either Gregory or the doctor as they moved about his cot. An odd thing happened when Gregory came to buckle wide canvas straps over the boy's body so that the surgeon could work upon his leg without danger of his jerking or twisting. Bart drew back into the narrow cot in sharp fright, making no show of bravery as he always had on everything else. For the first time he pleaded . . .

"Don't! Don't tie me!" he muttered in his throaty voice.

"But I must, so you don't move and ruin the bone setting. 'Tis just my father and I here," Gregory explained. "I shall stand beside you and you can hang onto my hand if you like," he went on comfortingly.

But Bart didn't know him and he pushed against the canvas and tore at the buckle on his chest with his good hand. "No, no!" he protested violently. "Untie me, untie me!" Then he added, "I'll hold still, I promise. I promise, Mr. Ben! Don't bind me!" his thick voice rose to a grim shriek and he pulled away from Gregory's intent, friendly face hard against the mattress.

Shocked, the surgeon's son drew back somewhat, a little hurt and much puzzled. His father brushed him aside with a quick shove and sat down on the opposite cot edge and unbuckled the top strap. To Gregory's questioning glance he responded softly, "He doesn't know you; he's partly delirious and thinks you're someone else." Then Stephen Donlewis took the boy's good shoulder in a firm hand and shook it slightly and gently slapped the right side of his face. "Bart!" he called firmly. "Listen to me. I'm a surgeon—remember? I have to fix your leg; you broke it. I'll not bind you after, understand, and there's nothing to fear. If you can hold still enough, I'll free you now. . . ."

The strange boy choked back his sobs; his eyes roved a little for a few seconds and then he tried to focus and seemed to come out of the thick haze of his delirium, for he muttered, "Greg?"

Gregory came around on the other side of the cot and touched his friend's forehead, pushing back wisps of scraggly hair. "I'm right here," he whispered.

Bart gritted his teeth and bit out a promise. "I will hold still!"

And he did . . . while Dr. Donlewis washed the leg with brandy, straight from the bottle. Though he came close to fainting, Bart grasped the cotside and did not fight against the doctor's firm, skilled fingers. White-faced, aware of the unavoidable pain he was causing, Dr. Donlewis cleansed the open part of the wound, for the fracture was compound. Then he got the bone edges together and taped them in place over linen and lint, after which he made a case of cerate plaster for the whole leg from knee to ankle. Before this process was half over, Bart was gray with pain and struggling against moaning. Gregory kept swallowing his saliva in great gulps; he had seen many people in pain but he somehow felt closer to Bart than he had to any other thus far. When his father began work on the ugly shoulder cut, from which infection oozed, Gregory chewed his lips viciously. Bart screamed at last as the surgeon débrided and bled the nasty cut.

Stephen Donlewis looked at Greg's pale face and suddenly reached out. Bart's head wobbled as the doctor's knotted fist connected swiftly with his jaw. The boy lay still at last and the surgeon could work faster. He sutured the wound two-thirds closed and then thrust a little wax cornucopia into the open end and set it firmly in place with bandage and court plaster, leaving an end free to drip upon a pad he affixed to the cot for that purpose. This, Gregory knew, was a type of seton and if it worked properly, it might help relieve the dangerous infection that was causing Bart's arm to swell with red stripes. Stephen Donlewis examined the underarm glands, which were puffed and hard. All of this would have caused Bart excruciating and exhausting pain. Knocking a patient out, however, was dangerous and sometimes had serious aftereffects. It was hard, often, for a surgeon to know which thing was better: to ease the pain and perhaps lose the patient or to let the patient suffer to the point of such hatred and fear that if he recovered he would never again have recourse to a doctor?

Afterward Dr. Donlewis brought Bart around by burning a sulphur stick under his nose. The boy sneezed on waking and groaned as he became conscious of his aches and pains.

"Stay with him, Greg," his father advised. "I'll send you some supper; and do you get broth and lemonade and vinegar water into him in whatever quantities you can!" And he went out to see a patient who now awaited him in the surgery.

Gregory kept the fire even and talked to Bart, who said his head felt twice its size. Later the strange boy began talking of the candle flames as drunken fireflies swooping across his eyes. Pretty soon he flushed under high fever and muttered and moaned; at length he struggled so to get out of bed that Gregory called his father.

The doctor put back the restraining straps and Bart went completely to pieces. The doctor himself pulled a chair to the cotside and sat beside the boy.

"You go do Monday's lessons so that you need not defile the Sabbath tomorrow," he ordered his son.

Gregory wondered if this order were entirely sincere or whether perchance his father did not want him to see his friend's suffering. It was probably something of both, for the Donlewises did keep Sunday carefully except for emergencies in surgery. The doctor worked over Bart until ten o'clock, washing him with alcohol, giving him a coolish clyster for his fever. Then, leaving Tullah on guard, he came into the kitchen for hot chocolate, which he shared with Gregory before sending him to bed.

"Strange thing about that boy, Meg," the surgeon muttered to his wife as she poured the whipped, frothy chocolate into thick mugs. "He is remarkably brave and sturdy, almost stoic; yet he went to pieces whenever we tried to strap him to the cot. Once he spoke a name, but not such as would help to identify him. Mr. Ben, I think he said."

Gregory nodded across the table.

"Why, for pity's sake, should a lad be afraid of being tied to a bed so as not to fall out of't? I did think he was not always delirious!"

Margaret Donlewis shook her head.

"Go get me the latest *Enquirer*," the doctor suggested suddenly.

Gregory ran off to the study; halfway there he knew why his father wanted the newspaper; he checked its pages swiftly coming back, squinting in the dimly lighted waiting room and surgery. There were no advertisements about runaways that week! The sharp-eyed surgeon, noticing the slightly disarranged pages and also his son's calm demeanor, grinned and said, "No need for me to look through this, I guess?"

"I think not, sir," Gregory grinned back at him.

"Go to bed, 'tis late enough," his father commanded. Not knowing the boy lingered over the paper in the passage, the surgeon continued to his wife while Greg was yet within earshot, "I'll sleep in the hospital, Meg; that boy's very bad. He's been half starved—for a lot longer than his sojourn in that shack I'd say."

"Beaten and abused, too, I suppose?" Mistress Donlewis wondered.

"No, I think not; he bears no marks to indicate abuse or flogging—our son is stamped more indelibly that way, at the moment," the doctor chuckled.

"He meant well, poor boy, and he was horribly humiliated. Shall you speak to Cecil Bodewell?" Margaret asked.

"Of course. I've already sent Keith to explain somewhat. As soon as I discovered the boy, after Keith followed Greg this morning and came home, I sent him back to the academy with a brief account," the doctor explained.

Gregory closed his bedroom door ever so softly. So that was how it had happened. And now what would become of Bart? Was it too late? Should he have told at the very first? He went to bed with almost as many fears and doubts as he had had the night before!

IX.

Bart Reaches the Turning Point

THE next morning Gregory, anxious for his friend, leaped out of bed at first call. He was permitted to wash Bart's face and hands and to help him into a clean cot for his reeked of his fever and was somewhat stained by drainage from the seton. The doctor affixed a new one and regarded the arm critically. The cut was not draining as well as the surgeon had hoped it would. Bart was too sick to eat anything at all.

After services and dinner the afternoon dragged slowly and Bart's fever mounted again, so that he had to be watched. At five o'clock Gregory broke down under the strain of the boy's moaning delirium. His father sent him out, as he had the night before.

The doctor did not come to supper with the family even though it was Sunday. Gregory supposed it was because he was concerned about Bart. About midevening Stephen Donlewis called for Gregory's help and he lanced Bart's arm. When they came out to the kitchen afterward, the doctor looked particularly heavy and anxious.

"Is . . . he . . . very bad?" Gregory choked out the question which had really been bothering him all day.

His father was nothing if not direct. He said, "Yes," simply.

"He won't die?" Gregory asked, not wanting to.

His father looked across the bowl of soup Launa had heated for him. "I don't know," he replied quietly and firmly.

Gregory burst into tears and ran toward the doorway

to the passage. The surgeon slammed a hand resoundingly on the table, shaking his soup bowl. "Come back here!" he called.

The boy stopped in his tracks and pivoted slowly. Margaret Donlewis sat straight up, arrested, with the sock she was knitting hanging limp from her fingers. The surgeon rose slowly from his chair and stood, as his son came back timidly to wait before him.

"He's your new friend, the boy there, and you love him as a boy does another boy who speaks on his terms and does within his ken, but Gregory, you want to be a doctor—you must learn something immediately, for you may be called upon, time and again, to treat someone you know and perhaps love well. I pray God I am a fair surgeon, but I am not infallible and neither shall you be, though you be one day better than I am. I make mistakes and there are a million things that I do not know. Mark me! If that boy should die this night, and he may——"

Gregory broke into thick sobs again and buried his face in his hands. "No, no! You must not let him die," he whispered.

His father grasped Gregory's arms with firm fingers. "Hear me! Death comes . . . and sometimes I can say why and more often I cannot. . . ." He shook the sobbing boy gently, steadying him on his feet afterward. "Stop crying and hear! If the lad dies, you must understand. . . . Death encroaches upon life softly, unheralded even, often enough; yet you cannot accept the idea of it when it is plain seen upon the horizon of a coming day? Control you, boy, or you'll do no studying in my surgery. Death is your sworn enemy and you must meet it head-on with your banners flying; you'll have as many defenses as any other doctor: whatever skill you've developed, whatever knowledge you've acquired, whatever native ability you can claim, whatever fortitude you muster, whatever in-

87

spiration you be given! Remember what I say: Death comes . . . and you must meet it."

Gregory struggled to swallow his feeling. When he could look levelly at his father, the surgeon released him. "Go on now to bed," he directed firmly. And he sat down and resumed his methodical consumption of his soup.

Gregory tiptoed away. In bed he snuggled close to Tawny and prayed a long while, brokenly as a boy will, that Bart would not die. And finally, before he was quite asleep, his mother came in, holding her little pewter candlestick.

"Asleep, Greg?" she whispered.

He twisted and pulled up into her arms as he had not done for a long while. "Oh, Mother, shall he die, the poor fellow?"

Margaret hugged him to her. "Surely not," she murmured. "But your father is right to be honest with you. I just thought that if you were awake you would want to know that he slept in the hospital last night, your father did—well, very likely he didn't sleep!—and he has gone in again to stay with the boy."

"Has he? I am glad . . . to know," Gregory said and then added thoughtfully, "he's meeting the enemy head-on, I expect."

"Yes!" his mother assured him.

Greg's father never afterward talked about that Sunday night in the hospital. He was drawn gray with sleeplessness the next morning and seemed rather cranky at breakfast. Gregory was afraid to ask about Bart, though he knew that the boy lived, for the doctor would have said if he had died during the night. Gregory went off to school in company with Keith for once; he wanted companionship; he kept up a picayune conversation all the way to the academy.

Greg would have come home with Keith, too, save that

the older boy had a special program to prepare and remained late after the last class. Gregory found Launa peeling turnips; he went off dutifully at her request for fresh water for supper. Then, after changing his clothes and putting up his books, he reported into the surgery, where he found his father tidying up after some minor treatments.

"Ah, so you have arrived," Stephen observed.

"Yes, sir. Shall I work on those jars of salve?"

"No, you may go in and see your friend—or should I say your charge, since you have saddled us with him," the doctor turned his mouth down rather wryly.

"Is he . . . better?" Greg was almost afraid to ask it.

"Yes, considerably better; the arm's clearing up," his father explained quietly, and Gregory's face lightened with his relief.

Bart was lying patiently with his ankles still tied to the foot of the cot so that he would not inadvertently kick at the leg cast. He smiled wanly at Gregory and talked a little about the warm comfort of the hospital room and asked what kind of day it was outside.

"I cain't never repay your father, Greg, fer what he's done fer me, for the times he's sat here wi' me, for the food, your clothes———"

"Hush, speak not of repaying us, and they are Keith's clothes." Gregory laughed, "Mine were too small!" But even he had noticed that the lad, despite his height, was gaunt to scrawniness, sunken-cheeked, ill fed.

After supper that night the doctor released Bart's feet, and he was able to move from side to side a little. Dr. Donlewis had closed the shoulder cut entirely and bandaged it. Bart could move his left fingers a little; his fever had abated; he no longer suffered from the horrible headache. He ate willingly everything that he was given. His leg ached constantly but he set his teeth against complaining, since so many of his other miseries had been alleviated. He was cheerful and hopeful. Gregory felt sure he had passed the danger point and was on the way toward recovery.

X.

Bart Fits In

As the week wore on, the hurt lad improved rapidly, until he could sit propped up the following Saturday afternoon. When occupied with mixing prescriptions or other tasks in the nearby pharmacy room, Gregory could sometimes wander in to talk to him; but when the doctor needed him in surgery, he knew his friend was lonely in the empty hospital room.

Sunday morning Gregory brought a big jar of pink pills into the hospital and spread them out on a clean cloth at the bottom of Bart's cot. He began counting them into small bottles.

"I wish I could help you," Bart whispered.

"Well, you can—I'll get you a basin and you can wash your hands and then help," Greg suggested.

Bart shook his head. "Naw, I cain't count. I know up to ten like the fingers on each hand but that's all."

Gregory stared at him, astonished. "Have you never been schooled?" he demanded.

"Naw, never. . . . 'Twas my mother taught me to ten and the letters of the alphabet, but I ain't never read none in books or anythin'. . . ."

"Well, then, 'tis high time you began. Can you write at all?"

Bart shook his head. All he could do was recite the numbers to ten and the alphabet, which small skill he demonstrated on demand. Gregory went into the pharmacy and dug for his old slate and slate crayon. He sat down on Bart's bed and wrote out the ten symbols for numbers:

$$0\ 1\ 2\ 3\ 4\ 5\ 6\ 7\ 8\ 9$$

"There, now see this, 'tis not difficult at all, for if you learn to make those ten figures, you can count to a million and more!" Greg explained.

"Truly, or do ye make sport o' me?" Bart wondered.

"Truly . . . for see here . . . after 9 you put 1 before each symbol and you go on for ten more, like this———" He wrote:

$$10\ 11\ 12\ 13\ 14\ 15\ 16\ 17\ 18\ 19$$

and then he illustrated each number with little piles of pills laid out carefully on the cloth. "Then you just do it all over again with 2 before the symbols and so on."

The strange boy was sharp-witted. He could manage to hold the slate with his mending left arm and he copied the ten symbols with painstaking precision. And it took only a few explanations for him to see the relationship between thirty, forty, and so on.

Greg was soon setting his friend problems in pills. The surgeon, wanting his son, looked in once and noticed the yellow head and the black bent in concentration over the little pyramids of pills as Bart counted five sets of ten pills each before putting the fifty in one of the small bottles. Stephen Donlewis smiled indulgently and went off without calling Gregory at all. The result of the boys' diligence was manifested the following week when Bart counted more pills, sutures, clean instruments and ligatures for the busy surgeon while Greg was at school. The lad was obviously bright and dependable; he made few errors and he even progressed rapidly with writing, once he tried. He made his figures carefully, perhaps too large but nonetheless accurate. By the end of the week following he was learning to read from an old primer; he had also graduated from hospital cot to the couch in surgery, where he could be useful counting, arranging trays of instruments, handing things when the doctor was alone and busy. Helped by Keith and the pair of crutches the doctor supplied, Bart began coming to two meals in the kitchen, also, with the rest of the family: breakfast and supper.

Actual reading the boy found a bit difficult, though he seemed anxious to master it. Gregory gave him some time every night before they went to bed, using the primer and then illustrating the letters and words in his carefully printed notes on pharmacopoeia. Soon, entirely out of the hospital room, Bart came to sleep on the other half of Greg's big bed; even the dog Tawny accepted him as a routine member of the household. He was fitting into the doctor's household almost as smoothly as a peg in a slot.

May was running out on them. No longer was there any need for fires except in the iron pharmacy basins. Bart's shoulder healed well and his leg was no longer painful; he rather longed to try his right foot on the surgery floor, but the doctor would not let him. However, Stephen Donlewis did permit the boy to sit on a high stool in the apothecary room for increasing lengths of time each day with his cast leg propped on another bench for part of the period and hanging for the rest of it.

Then, one Saturday night, Dr. Donlewis cut away the original cast and took off the dressing; the open wound had healed nicely. Bart watched, fascinated, this time as

Gregory prepared new cerate, making a solution of litharge in vinegar which, mixed with soap, oil and wax, formed into the proper consistency for spreading without heat.

Afterward, in the neat new cast which the doctor made, Bart began to spend more and more time in the pharmacy, where he learned many new things and practiced his letters by picking out the names of the preparations on the neatly stocked shelves. What fascinating names they were: calomel, turpentine, horehound, sulphur, Peruvian bark, tincture of saffron, gamboge, amber powder, jalap, aniseed, belladonna, tincture of myrrh, valerian, hartshorn, tartar, sassafras, foxglove, extract of butternut, burnt alum, mercurius dulcis—these were but a few of the ingredients in flint-glass bottles and pottery jars, in vials and jugs, in old, colored-porcelain containers—the collection of a lifetime truly. Also there were huge glass jars and bottles and crocks with alcohol, salt solution, vinegar, castor oil, ammonia, liquid laudanum, aromatic wine, gentian violet, limewater, oil of camphor, et cetera ... and mortars and pestles of various sizes and materials: stone, bronze, brass; the doctor's microscope, his distilling system, apothecary scales of several sizes with their graduating weights. Bart was never lonely in the pharmacy!

Every week Gregory brought the Richmond *Enquirer* home on his way from school on Saturday, when it was delivered to Jackson's General Store in Fairville; and every week the doctor scanned its pages openly before Bart, though this business had no immediate significance for the lad. The surgeon had questioned him only once, had bluntly asked for his name and origin. Bart had flushed in embarrassment, for the doctor had put the matter in no uncertain terms one day when the boy had stammered thanks to Gregory for a jacket of Keith's.

"I would know to whom we offer all this hospitality!"
Dr. Donlewis snapped at the boy.

Bart's face had reddened like a ripe apple.

"I'm asking who you are, boy, and where from?"

His face burning, Bart muttered, "I cain't say, I cain't
say, though I'd not displease yuh, suh!" Greg noticed that
his poor speech came through as it had not done for some
time, for the lad was rapidly imitating the better accent
and grammar of his new associates.

"Would you not displease me, eh?" the doctor had returned with eloquent sarcasm, but then he never pressed
the business further.

As time passed and there was nothing in the journal,
Gregory forgot how little they knew of the strange lad,
for about the surgeon's household everyone thought well
of him, servants, master, family alike—the diligent boy
who sought so eagerly to improve himself, who figured and
studied and progressed in better speech and manners by
leaps and bounds.

The last of May the doctor accepted the two students
he had earlier mentioned: Philip Coates and Edward
Yancey, serious fellows a year or so senior to Keith. The
surgeon set them a tough course in anatomy and physiology from which Gregory really benefited, too. Bart was
now capable with lots of routine services in the pharmacy.
This freed Gregory for more definitely medical pursuits
and studies. Both boys sometimes served as models in
the anatomy lectures, stripping and sitting or lying patiently while the two students named bones, blood vessels,
organs, pointing them out.

Keith came away from Bodewell's Academy right
proudly with the yearly prizes in both Greek and mathematics. The last day of his schooling there, Gregory and
Bart swept out the doctor's old black berlin and washed
its wheels and polished the brass fittings while Tullah

groomed Sultan, the chaise horse. The doctor and his wife were going to attend the exercises the senior students had planned.

"I'd be mighty proud to have schooling like Keith's and yours," Bart murmured, "but I reckon I could never master any of't."

"I'm not ungrateful, Greg," Bart added quickly, afraid that the surgeon's son would think him envious and bold to dream such dreams of scholastic achievement.

But Greg just nodded and said, "I know . . ." softly.

And the very next morning, though school was closed for the summer, Bart was a little startled to learn that in Dr. Donlewis's eyes the price of education was never fully met. For the surgeon told Gregory that his studies were not to be shelved by any means.

"You start Gregory on Xenophon this summer," the doctor ordered Keith. "There's no reason why he should not keep ahead of his class."

So, afternoons when it was hot and muggy and there were no patients in surgery, Keith and Greg curled up in the shade of the rocky knoll by the spring with the *Anabasis* between them. Sometimes when he was not too tired to hop and hobble that far, Bart joined them and lay on his stomach watching the water drip down to the brook; he enjoyed the fabulous retreat story in its translation and looked curiously at the cryptic Greek characters, wondering how the other lads made sense of them.

XI.

A Missing Needle

June melted into a taffy-sticky young July. Bart could get about on one crutch and he ventured now as far as the river road to watch the tobacco rollers going past to the town warehouses and the wharves on the river, the hogsheads bumping and bouncing, the rollers singing lustily.

Fourth of July brought a surprise visit from one of the older Donlewis boys: Alan, who was a lieutenant in the rather thin ranks of the very new United States Army. He had come from his station in Kentucky to surprise his mother. The unexpected arrival certainly did bring sparks of joy into her soft hazel eyes. The young man was handsome in his bright uniform and silk grenadier helmet. In fact Bart and Greg hung upon his every word with sudden interest in everything military. And for a couple of days after his departure Gregory went around whistling "Yankee Doodle," until his father caught him absently pouring liniment down the sides of a narrow-necked bottle while he tried to read a worn copy of *Treatise on a Captain's Duties to His Company,* which he had found stuffed in a corner somewhere, a remnant of Alan's West Point days.

"I'll doodle you for fair, boy!" the surgeon roared, pulling Greg's ear with one hand and stinging his behind with the flat of the other. "You will kneel on the second plank before the operating table and name me the bones of the arms and legs twenty-five times!"

Bart giggled. But he was sorry almost immediately,

for the strict surgeon credited no errors or stumblings, no slight hesitancies in order. Then almost as if Fate protested against the doctor's severity, a lenient mama indulged her spoiled son that afternoon, to the mutual disgust of both boys.

Mistress Akins from Cross Roads brought in her ten-year-old Timothy. He had been poking, like a busybody, in the haymow and had torn a gash four thumbs long in the back of his arm on a pitchfork. He was quite hysterical by the time they got him into the surgery, and nothing anyone could do or say would comfort him. Dr. Donlewis, not being given to more than normal persuasiveness, simply lifted the boy onto his big solid-oak operating table and strapped him down so that while he could still shriek, he could not thrash about.

"Do be quiet, Tim," Gregory pleaded. Sensing that the boy would not quit screaming for anything less than material gain, he added, "It's not going to hurt much. *Do you want my polished turtle shell?*" He had to out-shriek Timothy and somehow he managed. The boy pricked his ears at the notion of spoils. Gregory took advantage of the momentary silence and offered a velours tray of clean needles to his father.

"No, I've my own polished turtle shell now," Timothy reported superiorly and promptly set his mouth for another scream.

"My peach-pit basket?" Greg suggested.

"No!"

The needles in the case looked interesting; as the surgeon reached for a curved steel one, the Akins boy followed his hand with his eyes. "Say, what are those?" he asked.

"Surgical needles." Gregory explained.

"I'd like one of those!" Timothy said. "That one on the end—it looks like 'tis gold!"

"Yes," Gregory admitted.

"Well, if you give me that, I'll not scream!"

"Don't be silly," Gregory replied, as he might have to a four-year-old.

Dr. Donlewis stuck the needle he had just threaded into a fold of his shirt sleeve where it would be handy. He reached out firm fingers for Timothy's arm. The boy, remarking his mother's intent and anxious face, screamed delightfully.

"Timmy, deah," Mistress Akins moaned pityingly.

"I'll be brave if he gives me the pretty gold needle! It looks like a Tripoli pirate's scimitar."

"Oh, Timmy, I don't think . . ." Mistress Akins hesitated with minor embarrassment, but then she said hopefully to the doctor, "of course, if he really thinks it would help him to bear the pain?"

Dr. Donlewis looked over toward the fussy little woman and almost grinned. "Nonsense!" he exclaimed firmly as he thrust his steel needle in the first stitch.

Timothy howled. The surgeon gestured Gregory to tie the loop, after which he cut the thread and took the second stitch and then the third, all to the furious accompaniment of Timothy's shrieks.

"Finish that," the doctor ordered Gregory, releasing the bandaging he had started on Timothy's arm to his son. Then the surgeon took the case of needles and returned it to the top drawer of the small walnut cabinet he kept beside the operating table.

Gregory finished the bandaging and undid the operating-table straps. Timothy sat up and hung his feet off and waited for his mama to help him down.

"I'll want to see the arm Friday," the doctor closed the business.

As Timothy went out, holding his mother's hand, big boy that he was, Bart smirked at Gregory and curtsied

98

with the flaps of his vest. Both boys giggled gleefully as soon as the Akinses were out of earshot.

"Go warm wax to make bougies, Greg," the doctor ordered into this merriment, "and Bart, you clean the gentian violet from that bowl with alcohol."

The incident was forgotten until Timothy's return on Friday, this time accompanied by the Akins butler. Before the doctor came from the hospital room, where he had a fever patient, Timothy teased Greg incessantly for the gold needle. And though Bart, who was sitting on the couch in the surgery, cutting and measuring lengths of suture, protested, the bold little boy opened the top drawer of the surgeon's cabinet and stood admiring the article of his desire. He shoved the drawer shut swiftly when he heard the doctor approaching. Stephen Donlewis cut the stitches in the boy's arm, dressed it lightly, accepted his normal fee from the butler, and sent the boy home.

About four days later the doctor ordered Coates to thread the curved gold needle; it was not in its proper place in the velvet-lined tray. A diligent search of surgery, pharmacy, hospital room, and study failed to produce the missing implement. Reflection assured the surgeon that he had not used the needle since the day before young Timothy's last visit. It was logical therefore that Gregory, remembering that the boy had pestered him, should propose that young Akins had pilfered the object he had so much desired. In this opinion Greg was firmly supported by Bart, who told how Timothy had fumbled with the tray in the drawer.

Continual discussion among all the lads, Keith, Greg, the two students and Bart, about the likelihood of young Akins' having taken the needle resulted at length in working the surgeon up to the point where he consented to the idea of Keith's going to the Akins plantation and inquiring as diplomatically as he could as to whether such might have been the case. Keith insisted afterward that he had been tactful and pleasant and had asked whether, without thinking, Timothy might have popped the needle in his pocket while admiring it. No one foresaw the effect this intimation would have upon Mistress Akins. She came storming from Cross Roads immediately in her light chaise after Keith on the doctor's bay mare. She fairly stomped into the surgeon's waiting room, not even bothering to see if there were patients.

"How dare you accuse my son of stealing!" she shouted.

It took all the doctor's self-control to persuade her that no one had intended such an accusation but that since he fancied the gold needle, he had just sent his son to make inquiry.

"Well, 'twill be a sick day indeed at Akins plantation before we send for you again!" the angry dame cried, and swirled out in a flurry of rustling flounces, her feathered poke bonnet a bit awry on her short, rolled curls.

Whereupon Stephen Donlewis caught his youngest son in hand and hauled him behind the closed door of the study. "Now see here, young man, mind your tongue next time. A patient is a patient! And it behooves a doctor to consider his own feelings nil in his dealings with one. So I have lost the needle. 'Twas not for you to work everyone up against somebody without proof. Had you any proof? Any at all?"

"No, sir, save that Bart thought he saw Timothy slip his hand in his pocket after he had touched the top drawer!"

"Bart! Bart this and Bart that—I've had enough of Bart. Think you not, perhaps, since you must accuse, that he might have hidden the needle himself among his few things?" For they had given Bart a cabinet in the apothecary shop and he had collected there some empty boxes and scraps of paper, leaves, stones, and other sundries that a boy cherishes.

"Why would Bart take it?" Greg protested.

"Because 'tis gold and, as it has many a poor fool, the word alone would intrigue him falsely as to its value."

Gregory came to his friend's defense. "He'd never do such a thing!"

"Would he not? What do we know of him?" the surgeon demanded.

Gregory admitted thickly, "Nothing, really . . ."

"Exactly. Now mark me well, you have grown too fond of the fellow. I'm certain that he's a runaway and generally a boy that will run from one thing will run from another. I don't want you hurt someday because you've put your faith in him."

Greg was not easily discouraged about his friend. "Might he not have run from an unhappy home where he was not wanted?" he suggested.

"Yes, except that he did not," the surgeon returned with force. "You are still not very observant, despite my tutoring. His hands are so calloused that I expect he has worked with a joiner or a cooper or a cordwainer, which would indicate that he has run from a master," the doctor explained. "That is why I have been watching the advertisements in the *Enquirer* so carefully. Now then, stay from supper tonight and examine his cabinet, understand?"

Gregory agreed politely, though he was reluctant to do the task. And when he did open the compartment to look through Bart's few pitiful affairs, his face burned hot—especially when he noticed the butterfly-wing pin carefully wrapped in a clean puff of the doctor's lint, yet trustfully left on the cabinet shelf in a fold of brown paper. To his inner content, Greg found no needle, which fact he reported happily to his father while Bart was occupied scrubbing some utensils outside.

"Greg, just watch the lad well; I would but save you from having your faith bruised, for that be a wound no surgeon can heal very readily."

XII.

The Needle Recovered

THE end of that week, after supper Friday, Dr. Don-lewis called Bart into the surgery and had him set his right leg upon the floor, putting aside his crutch. The boy trembled under his own weight and the leg felt fragile and prickly. Bart took a few short steps and stumbled against the couch.

"Practice now and then when you think of moving or must; carry the crutch but try not to use it," the doctor offered advice.

Bart did practice diligently and kept any discomfort to himself. Saturday afternoon Gregory went to the mill for their new supply of flour, for he had left Malcolm's grain to be ground on Thursday. Keith was at Merry-haven observing the management of the factor's office, in which he was much interested. Plantation direction fascinated him as the surgery fascinated Gregory.

The surgeon, needing chips for an apothecary fire, called Gregory and then remembered that the boy was off at the miller's. The doctor shouted up the passage, supposing Keith to be in his room, but Tullah called down that the young man had gone to his uncle's plantation. The surgeon resorted to Bart, called for him ringingly, in fact. There was no answer. Returning through the surgery to the waiting room, the doctor next shouted outside loudly enough to provoke reply from Launa in the kitchen garden.

"Bart be not about, massa!"

"Well, where the devil can he have gone?" the surgeon muttered to himself, looking down the drive and then over toward the knoll. He finally had to ask Tullah to chip the soft pine wood for the fire. Afterward he sent the servant to seek Bart; Tullah returned in due course to report that he had looked just about everywhere and turned up no one. Gregory came home from the mill with Malcolm's donkey and unloaded the heavy flour sacks. Then he went in to see his father immediately and find out whether anything new had come up in surgery.

At about that same time, heralded by a burst of summer thunder, the two students returned from a trip to Petersburg. They pulled out the doctor's carefully delineated anatomy charts in preparation for an examination he intended to give them that very night. They had not seen Bart since an hour before their departure for Petersburg just before lunch. Greg now searched everywhere anxiously until the storm mounted the western sky and broke nastily over the town. The hot ground steamed under the pounding, lightning-gashed rain and sudden gusts of wind.

"So the scrawny chicken has flown the coop?" the doctor asked when Greg reported that his diligent search had provided no news of Bart's whereabouts. "He might at least have waited until we put some more flesh on him!"

"Do you think he has gone—gone away?" Gregory queried.

"Yes, and I've rather been expecting that he would! However, I like not that he's gone with my cast still upon his leg, half healed under my doctoring, and I don't intend that he shall get far enough to attest any incompetency of mine in the matter. As soon as Keith returns, you two will hitch up the pony to the cart and go find him—and don't come back until you have. The ungrateful pup shall not run from me without my blessing on't!" the doctor roared.

Keith had left Merryhaven before the storm broke, so he stopped part way home at a school friend's to avoid a drenching. Setting out from there as soon as the rain stopped, he reached home before the puddles had soaked into the front driveway. Greg was waiting with the cart; the two boys set out upon the doctor's order as soon as Keith got the pony into the traces. The blue sky was more burnished after the rain as the sun shone hot again. Shiny puddles mirrored the wispy strays of cloud that followed the storm. Mute evidence of the force of the brief storm lay all about: broken twigs, torn leaves, soaked branches with their foliage shining against the muddy road.

"Surely he could not have got far in that downpour," Keith declared as he clucked to the pony.

"Go by way of Cross Roads; Coates and Yancey just came up from Halfway House and saw no trace of him and you yourself would have noticed anyone making shelter on the river road," Dr. Donlewis directed Keith from the waiting-room steps.

So they went northwest toward Stony Creek, past the tavern and Mistress Serdom's dame school along the road that led toward the James on the south bank heading west. The roadside was not much overgrown. Bart could hardly be hidden there without being seen, nor could he duck successfully from passers-by. Since he limped badly, he would be set out for notice. Sure enough, the blacksmith at the fork toward Stony Creek remembered seeing him pass before the storm, so the boys knew they were headed in the right direction. Then, not much farther on, they remarked the boy's lean figure up ahead, almost stumbling—but oddly, he was coming back toward Fairville!

Keith pulled up the pony. A more miserable sight than poor Bart could scarce be imagined. He was soaked to the skin and his clothes clung to him, sopping; in fact, he quite literally dripped. His hair had come untied and was hanging stringily about his neck; he could barely walk even with the help of a stout stick he had broken from some handy source. He fell gratefully into the cart as soon as he recognized Greg and Keith. Neither of the Donlewises had the heart to question him or to scold. Keith just headed the pony around and drove back home.

"You are a wretched spectacle," Gregory observed and he thought Bart gave a sort of sob of acquiescence.

Keith drove directly to the waiting-room door, to which the doctor came as soon as he heard the pony's short gait. Greg ran around the side of the cart and offered his friend an arm, but the surgeon stepped down, shoved his son aside, lifted the boy out of the cart in his arms and carried him in to the couch in the surgery.

"Fine specimen, aren't you?" the doctor began, low and icily. He looked immediately at the soaked, crumbling, rather soggy cast.

Bart winced at the surgeon's touch. He ached intolerably clear up into his back and was so taken with shivers that the doctor poured him out a modicum of good rum and ordered Gregory to make him hot tea with honey.

"If you don't come down with lung fever as a result of your pigheadedness, I'll stand surprised," the doctor stated. "What use shall you be to yourself or anyone else if you spend your lifetime running? Scarce healed of one evil, you create yourself another. Discontent, boy, begets trouble on a mountainous scale, as yeast raises up a mass of dough. I made you as comfortable as might be and have led you no more rough a time of it than I have my own sons. Drink this!"

Bart made a wry face and coughed on the strong liquor, but it warmed him deeply. The doctor had already stripped off his wet clothes and bundled him into a dry flannel shift. The boy sat, wan, in the white gown like a bit of a ghost plunked upon the gray-serge couch cover; two large, silent tears crept down his rain-stained cheeks. The doctor went on scolding, ignoring them.

"I have to cut off that cast now and see what damage you've done. Like as not you've jarred the setting and shall suffer the whole trouble over again, which you doubtless deserve!" The surgeon selected a small saw from his cabinet and spread an old copy of the *Enquirer* on the couch; he lost no time. "Lie back; it won't hurt," he stated but his harsh tone was not very reassuring.

Bart dropped back and lay with his fists clenched; the small saw chugged into the crumbling cerate mixture.

"I'd not scold, boy, if you'd aught to run from, but you've spoken a few times of being grateful; is this then your gratitude, that you run off attesting illy of my skill when I've not dismissed you? We've treated you fair enough, considering; did you know, for instance, that my son was caned before an hundred of his fellow students on your account, because you were too stubborn to admit of your condition and let him summon me?"

Bart murmured a choked "No, suh," and began to cry softly.

"Ah, I thought not; you didn't know that, nor yet that I gave him a wretched forty-eight hours when I dismissed him from my service because he would not speak openly. 'Twas you he promised against such candor, was't not?" The saw kept slipping off the crumbling wax, but the doctor was making progress down the length of the cast, even breaking off bits with his fingers. "Well?" he roared.

And Bart answered, "Y—yes, suh," feebly.

The cast fell apart with a final faint crackle and the doctor unwound the interior dressing; then he hummed a little and pressed the leg all around. "It looks all right," he admitted, though the boy cringed under his pressure. "I shall splint it and put you back on crutches for a couple of days and then we'll see. All this trouble for naught because you would run off and try your weight in the world alone again—I know your kind, eternally flitting from decent labor and honest effort!"

Tears were running fast down the boy's cheeks now and he finally could bear the doctor's angry voice no longer. "Please . . ." he cried, "why do you say I ran off? I was coming back—I tried to get back before the storm but I fell—and I was feared for my leg and then the rain started—why, oh, why have you not asked where I went and what I did!" he burst out; and he laid open his right fist before the doctor's eyes. In it was a sliver of gold, the curved needle. Stephen Donlewis met the boy's blue eyes; the doctor's color rose slowly. Gregory, coming in with the mug of hot tea, stared.

"I knew that Timothy Akins took it—I saw him! And I knew, too, that you thought I did, that you did not trust me," the boy explained, barely above a whisper.

"How did you come to believe that?" the surgeon asked.

"Because someone searched my cabinet and did not put my things back quite the way I had 'em." He was a sharp enough lad.

"Greg did because I ordered it," the doctor acknowledged.

"Well, I vowed to go find that Akins the first day I could manage—and that storm come up——"

"Came—came up," Gregory thrust in.

The sound of a carriage came from the drive. A moment later Tullah announced from the waiting-room door, "Mistress Akins, Doctor!" And Gregory gave a faint groan as that lady came sweeping to the surgery rail.

But she was most gracious. "I wish to apologize, Dr. Donlewis. I had no idea that Timothy had really taken your needle. I am glad your apprentice had the courage to set him right and retrieve it."

The doctor replied carefully, "Bart is not my apprentice but a patient still staying on. . . ."

Mistress Akins smiled so pleasantly that her straw bonnet looked downright becoming. "I see. Well, I was going to compliment you on your good fortune in having got yourself such a strong-spirited, righteous fellow," she nodded toward Bart, who lifted himself on his palms and spoke her a polite "good afternoon."

And thus the gold needle went back to repose in its velours case and Dr. Stephen Donlewis was given pause in some of the unkind things he had thought about the strange boy.

XIII.

Want Ads and a Toothache

THE following weekend Dr. Donlewis was able to remove the splints from Bart's leg. Each day the boy walked increasingly better. By mid-August, when Malcolm Donlewis was harvesting his barley, Bart could manage to go around the perimeter of the field without tiring. Soon he was tramping across Fairville to Jackson's to pick up the papers and other packets or letters that came on the post chaise from Richmond on Saturday morning. He relieved Gregory of this task and many others; he offered, in fact, to scrub the surgery and wash the accumulated towels and reusable bandages every day, but at that the surgeon balked. Gregory would do whatever was required of every surgical apprentice. Bart, however, became better at figures and was very useful in the apothecary field, thus releasing Gregory to more serious studies.

The summer days swooped past. In early September Keith made several trips to Williamsburg in connection with his enrollment in the college; he became so preoccupied with fashion that Margaret Donlewis cut out clothes and supervised sewing for ten full days. During this process she sent for Bart one Saturday morning and measured him from stem to stern, though he protested, embarrassed.

"You've need of a good set of clothes and 'tis better we make them now than that we remember you too late and must needs weave a new web of cloth," she replied, smiling at him gently.

"But I cannot pay for them nor yet for your trouble," he remonstrated.

"Don't you do what you're given to do? Have you never thought that Greg should have all that, too, and much less time for his Greek and his anatomy?"

Bart rubbed one toe over the other, a habit he had acquired since he had laid away his crutch for good. "No'm," he murmured.

"Well, then, and you are fond of Greg?"

"You know well that I am, yes'm," he said to that.

"Would you be seen with him in poor clothes and shame him?"

"No'm."

"Hold still, boy! And 'tis high time you got those

bare feet into stockings and shoes before fall chill. I'll remember to have Launa set that good pair of shoes Arne has outgrown before your bed tonight—there, now you may run on," she put aside her measuring tape and released him.

But he stood a moment as even a big boy will sometimes, with his lips slightly parted as though he would say some momentous thing, but then nothing at all succeeded. He finally went out from the small sewing room.

"Did you fetch the *Enquirer* this morning?" the doctor asked as Bart passed through the surgery to return to the cough syrup he had been mixing.

"Yes, sir, 'tis on your desk in the study; I'll get it," and he did.

The surgeon wiped his hands on a handy towel and sat down to relax for a few minutes in an old red-leather chair. Gregory was cleaning up odds and ends of dressings and medicines. Philip Coates went into the pharmacy to get the doctor's basket of bones, from which he had been ordered to construct a complete skeleton. He set about this task in a corner of the surgery behind the railing. Bart came out to watch him; taking his stand beside the doctor's chair, he occasionally glanced from the skeleton construction to the page of the journal. Stephen Donlewis noticed Bart's lips moving once as he struggled to read some of the words.

"Making progress with your reading, eh? Perhaps I'll not have to read this for your benefit each week?" the surgeon teased, and Coates and Gregory both burst out laughing.

Bart did not understand and said so. Dr. Donlewis just chuckled dryly himself, folded the paper and dropped it on the couch. He went into his study to prepare his saddlebags for some house calls he had to make. Bart looked toward Coates because Gregory was counting and sorting instruments. "What is the *Enquirer?*" Bart wondered. " 'Tis not like a book?"

Coates shook his head. " 'Tis a newspaper; 'tis printed twice each week so that folk who are interested may find out what is going on: which men shall run for governor, who died, what is happening in Europe . . . and locally, too—see here," the young man left his half-completed skeleton and took the paper from the couch. "See, it says here that St. Thomas's Church will hold a fair the end of the month———"

"What did the doctor mean that he reads for my benefit?" Bart inquired.

"Oho, you didn't get that?" Coates laughed again and Gregory looked up sharply. "He doubtless thinks you ran away—did you? I've always meant to ask since Keith told me how they found you in that shack!"

Gregory watched his friend with interest, expecting sudden anger, but Bart's mouth just lined straight. Coates did not pursue his query but explained, "Generally, folk advertise for lost animals, missing apprentices, and so on, or even things they would like to buy. The paper runs these items under the headings WANTED or LOST. See, here's such a notice," he pointed and read off:

> LOST, the 6th instant, black filly, with one white foreleg, nervous, lively, has an uneven gait. Anyone restoring said animal to the subscriber, Todd Hayman, Manchester, or giving advice leading to recovery shall have FOUR DOLLARS REWARD.

Bart just murmured, "Oh," and never said anything to Gregory at all but returned quietly to his work. But from then on he begged Greg to help him nights by candlelight with his primer and other books, and he saved pages from old *Enquirers* and practiced picking out whole paragraphs, working slowly and painstakingly to get their sense.

As September drew on, the doctor steered relentlessly toward the completion of his courses for his son and the two students. The latter, like Keith, were due to enter colleges in late October or early November, whereas Bodewell's Academy would open the last week in September. The surgeon demanded scholastic excellence from all three lads but, Bart noticed, it was from his son alone that he asked physical assistance. And it was Greg who went more often on outside calls those weeks before school and sometimes he came back looking upset and tired. Bart wondered.

Then, one Tuesday afternoon, a patient so badly injured that he required twelve stitches in one leg and five in the other was brought in. Gregory did the five alone, since Coates and Yancey had gone to market with Mistress Donlewis in the chaise. Bart ran errands between surgery and pharmacy. The keen-eyed boy noticed immediately that his friend was nervous and upset and slow; in fact, Greg bit the lower inside of his lip to shreds before he finished. His father observed him keenly but made no remarks—that is, until the patient had been taken home by his friends. Then the air in the surgery became blue for a few moments.

"Would you be a surgeon or not?" the doctor cried. "You've to get over this nonsense of getting sick and trembling like a man with the ague!"

"I'm sorry!" Greg protested. "Did I take the stitches badly?"

"Too deep twice and agonizingly slow. If I'd been that slow with the twelve, the poor man would be suffering yet!"

This made Gregory wince and knot his hands. And Bart looked so worried that the doctor snarled at him.

"Hang your sympathy on the clothesline, boy! Sorry's never mended anything yet!"

After supper the two boys shelled nuts for Launa outside the kitchen door and talked earnestly. It was Bart who brought up the experience of the afternoon.

"Greg, what was the matter with you today?" he asked. "In the surgery, I mean."

"The same old thing," Greg admitted, biting his lip again.

"What same old thing?"

"I always have it—I go to pieces when I have to hurt someone, and yet I want to be a doctor like my father and help people—I do want to!"

Bart looked at him fully. "You don't always go to pieces," he stated. "You didn't wi' me in the shack, remember—and you had to hurt me plenty, too."

Greg opened his mouth a moment in surprise but then he said, "I got sick once, after I left you——"

"That's different; I was the patient and I never knew it! You didn't act upset and nervous before me."

Gregory thought about it a moment. "Well, it was different with you, because I had to do it, don't you see? There was nobody else!"

Bart smiled at him. "You've just said it! Don't you realize that you always have to do it?"

"No," Gregory shook his head, "I don't see that at all."

"Well, 'tis true and you should see it; in fact, you must see it; that's what your father wants you to see. Every time with every case it is the same thing—you have a decision to make and it's yours, not your father's; he can teach you what to do but he can never do it for you."

"Must you preach and scold at me too?" Greg grumbled.

So Bart said, "No," and popped a hazelnut in his mouth.

The very next afternoon, it being Wednesday, the doctor went off to his plantations with the two students; after school Gregory helped Bart make Whyte's tincture, which was a rather elaborate process.

It began to rain in late afternoon and dusk came early. The surgeon did not return before it had fallen. Bart lighted the lanterns in surgery and waiting room and Tullah lighted the one at the entrance to their drive. A few moments later a wagon rumbled up outside the waiting room. The man who descended from it was big and gruff.

"Where be the surgeon?" he demanded of Bart, who opened the door for him.

"Not back yet from the plantations he serves."

"I can't wait—I've to get on, but I can't hardly see to drive with the toothache. If you be the doctor's apprentice, get you a pliers and yank this danged thing out!"

"I'm not the doctor's apprentice but I'll get him," Bart offered.

The man stomped restlessly up and down before the railing.

"But I've never pulled a tooth," Gregory protested in a whisper when Bart told him.

The bigger boy shrugged. "There's always a first time," he said.

"You mean you think I should do it! Surely he can wait. Father'll be back shortly."

"You talk to him." Bart suggested.

So Greg did, hoping secretly that the man would immediately decide he was too young or too small to be considered as tooth puller. But the wagoner was really anxious to get on.

"I've to get to Norfolk before I put up. Now get your pliers, boy, and oblige me. I ain't scared, if ye be not. Ye look strong enough and yer friend here can gi' ye a hand too!"

Gregory swallowed uncomfortably but Bart giggled.

"I—I can't——" Gregory began but Bart thrust in.

"He can't treat you out here; come sit in this big chair and put your head back." Efficiently Bart ushered the man through the railing, took off his woolen jacket, settled him in the leather armchair, and pulled the light down.

Gregory came through the railing.

" 'S this . . . ugh . . . ugh . . ." the man grunted.

Bart waved three different pliers from the instrument cabinet and thus aided Gregory in the first important decision. The doctor's son nodded at the one he thought would work. "You'd better get on with it," Bart mouthed, "before your father finds you hesitating."

This was almost as formidable an idea as pulling the tooth. Gregory had seen lots of tooth pullings. He wondered whether he had the strength to cope with the big molar the wagoner was indicating.

"Come on, boy, ye can't hurt me any worser'n she do already!" the man muttered.

Gregory took the pliers, adjusted the light and set about grasping the tooth. Bart breathed in relief and stood ready to help in any way he could. Twice the pliers slipped before Gregory could even try to loosen the tooth, but finally he got a good firm grip with both hands. He felt the molar move slightly and he braced his knee against the chair. Quite suddenly he became occupied with the business at hand, so much so that he did not hear horses outside.

Taking in the scene immediately, Dr. Donlewis sent Coates for a basin and a moment later he added his strength to his son's by putting his hand over the boy's. One yank more and the tooth was out!

"Good boy!" the doctor commented after the man had gone on his way with his jaw packed with cotton and a bit of old blanket wrapped around his head as protection against the weather. "First time I've ever seen you take something on alone!"

Gregory looked toward Bart and would have spoken, but his friend just winked at him.

XIV.

The Doctor's Dilemma

GREGORY went back to school the next Monday. Every morning Bart walked part way down the road with him beside Patches; and if he were not at an assigned task, he went to meet the surgeon's son in the late afternoon. Generally the autumn days were clear and gay with color, and were full of enjoyment, what time the two lads had of them together. Bart now did much of the cleaning and scrubbing, particularly during Greg's school hours, though Saturday afternoons the doctor's son was never spared. The students were slaving at their anatomy and physiology. Keith was studying mornings in review and helping out in the factor's office at Merryhaven afternoons, impatient now for the college classes to begin. All the Donlewises took Bart for granted now and the students regarded him as they might have some poor cousin attached to the doctor's household. Margaret Donlewis treated the lad much as she had all her own boys before him; everyone had apparently forgotten the mystery of his arrival. Only the surgeon remained strictly formal with him, and cool; yet even he had stopped searching the notices in the journal.

Then one day Ed Yancey knocked upon the doctor's study door and was bade in. "Excuse me, sir, but I was reading an item in last week's *Enquirer* and I noticed that you'd cut out a bit on the other side and if 'twould not be any trouble, could I borrow the slip?" the lad asked. "I was reading about the comet, you know, sir, and 'tis all quite interesting—'twill be readily seen here from dark after the fifth of October, they say."

"I cut nothing from the paper; in fact I read it but cursorily yesterday, and intended a better perusal since I find this comet business interesting myself," the doctor returned.

"Well, someone has cut a portion out neatly, with a razor-sharp instrument—see here," Yancey proffered the sheet in question. The doctor glanced at it swiftly. The rectangular hole was between two notices: one about a sale of ironmongery, the other a reward for the return of a strayed mule.

Dr. Donlewis humphed and shrugged. Yancey went off, leaving the mutilated paper on the desk. As soon as he was out of earshot, the surgeon sent for Arne and handed him the page. "Go get me another copy of this paper at Jackson's if he has any left from Saturday. If not, get him to locate one from a subscriber somewhere that I may borrow to read and see what was cut out," he ordered.

That night the two students, Greg, and Bart were all gathered in the surgery to watch an interesting setting of a comminuated leg fracture. As the doctor wrapped the splints, he occasionally asked one or another of the lads to hand him something. "Greg, get me that basin . . . Yancey, that roll of tape . . . Coates, the small shears," and presently he ordered, quite casually, "Worrell, give me the court plaster."

And Bart picked up the roll from the cabinet top, turned toward the surgeon, then caught himself sharply. Stephen Donlewis looked evenly at him, a long, level glance across the operating table; it was enough.

"Stand at the cabinet there and don't move!" the surgeon directed harshly after receiving the court plaster from the boy's hand; as Bart had moved to hand the roll across the table, he had reddened gradually until he was as ruddy as a ripe love apple. He stood as he was ordered; the hot flush continued to dye his face.

Eventually the doctor sent his patient home in his carriage with the two students watching over the newly splinted leg. When only Greg remained, sweeping and picking up, Dr. Donlewis plucked a copy of the *Enquirer* from a shelf along the surgery wall and tossed it toward Bart.

"Now, then, demonstrate that you can read what I have underscored in red," the surgeon commanded.

Bart's hands shook, holding the newspaper, as he choked out the words one after the other, painfully:

WANTED—Information as to whereabouts of one JEBART WORRELL, indented cooper's apprentice who ran away from the subscriber before the past trimester; he is 14 years old, lanky and lean, of a lightish countenance with yellow hair; he eloped in serviceable clothes of broadcloth and fustian. Whoever shall take up said boy or arrange for his return to his master shall have a reward of TWENTY-FIVE DOLLARS. Be it advised it is forbid harboring or trusting such a runaway.

BEN MOPES

Manchester, Sept. 27   w 4t

"You are the subject of said advertisement, I take it?" the surgeon asked and Bart hung his head in acquiescence. "Where is the piece you cut from my first paper?"

The lad fished it out of the inner pocket of his new jacket that Mistress Donlewis had just finished. "You didn't have to make me stand beside the cabinet, sir; I'd not have run away," he muttered pridefully.

"Would you not have?" the doctor growled. "Then suppose you explain now, at long last, exactly why you ran from your master four months ago!"

Bart looked hard at the much-scrubbed planking of the surgery floor and made no answer.

"Speak!" the surgeon urged in no uncertain tone of command.

But Bart remained silent.

"Tell us, Bart, please; we are your friends!" Gregory pleaded, leaning anxiously upon the corn broom.

"Commit not me so!" his father snapped sourly, and Greg colored pink for his friend's feelings. "Boy, answer, you hear?" the doctor raised his voice and Bart cowered a little. "Were you mistreated? Unjustly beaten?"

Bart muttered a sullen "No."

"You're honest at least," the doctor observed, "for I could have told, were you beaten. Were you then poorly sheltered and ill fed?"

To this question the surgeon rather expected an affirmative reply but the strange lad again mumbled a firm negative.

"You refuse to speak anything of it?" Stephen Donlewis asked; Gregory felt sure that a negative response from Bart would induce the doctor to close the whole business.

Bart just stood stubborn, his head still hanging.

"I've harbored you innocent; I'll not keep you twenty-four hours under my roof, knowing you delinquent. I have to go into Richmond tomorrow afternoon to pay an apothecary bill of long standing. I shall stop at your master's in Manchester on my way and arrange for your return to him. Shall I be able to trust you to remain here, properly clothed and ready until I return, at which time I shall dispatch you with Tullah?" Stephen demanded. "Reply!" he very nearly shouted for it appeared that Bart would continue to stare at the floor as though the sanded boards particularly interested him.

Without really raising his head, the lad acknowledged at last, "I will do . . . whatever you wish, sir. . . ."

"Go to bed!"

Bart ran out as though relieved to put the surgeon's icy voice and stern face away from him. Gregory listened for the bedroom door to close; then he plucked at his father's sleeve and the surgeon turned to him.

"Can't we do—something?" the boy murmured.

"We can be arraigned for sheltering him!" the doctor bit out fiercely.

"I mean—well—he's been helpful to us; maybe this man, this Mr. Mopes, doesn't really want him back?"

"Therefore he offered a twenty-five-dollar reward—and paid out several hundred dollars for the indenture in the first place?" the doctor smiled upon his son, though a bit grimly.

"He has fortitude, Bart," Greg put forth carefully. "Surely he didn't run from a simple matter?"

"An angry face, a cross word, poor fare, though he didn't admit it—he may have run from any such," the doctor huffed. "Mark me, generally a boy who will run from one will run from another, and I'm of no sympathy with that type at all. No apprentice may expect a bed of roses! Greg, you must learn to pick and choose among your friends and not hang your heart so open upon your shirt sleeve," the doctor put out his hand and pulled at one of his son's curls teasingly.

But Greg was not much comforted. "I want for him not to go!" he protested.

The doctor coughed dryly. "My mind is set. You may come with me tomorrow, if you like. I cannot leave until I return from the plantations and you should be from school by then. Now, let's make an end to the whole affair." He turned from the surgery and went into his study and closed the door.

Gregory finished sweeping, washed under the operating table with vinegar water, and dusted the area, after it dried, with clean sawdust. Then he went to his bedroom. Bart seemed to be asleep. The surgeon's son was hurt by what he supposed was an easy indifference that would allow his friend to sleep at such a crisis in his life. But Greg looked carefully before he extinguished his candle and he knew then that Bart was not really asleep. Perhaps he could not bear the thought of talking. The surgeon's son could only accept his friend's terms.

Ironically it was a beautiful day, the next, born out of a low dawn with a thick, dripping fog. The autumn sun brushed the countryside with glitter in the late afternoon, burnishing the yellows of birch and poplar, the reds, oranges, and saddle browns of other deciduous trees, polishing the sturdy evergreens until they shone like glass, buffing the scarlets to a velvety gloss. Gregory, always much affected by the weather, felt his spirits rebound in spite of himself—and was conscience-smitten en route to Richmond whenever he thought of the lad he had left behind. For Bart had gathered up his few things in an old knapsack that Keith had found for him; then he had put on his best clothes: his new white-flannel shirt—like Greg's, made to the surgeon's design—his just-finished serge trousers and vest, the fustian jacket that had been

Alan's before West Point and which, though cut slightly old-fashioned, was as good as brand-new. Upon the doctor's command, Tullah had clipped the boy's hair short like Keith's in the new style, for Bart would soon be fifteen. Banned now from the apothecary room and any work, feeling outcast already, the lad sat glum beside the fireplace in the kitchen, picking out sentences in Greg's copy of *Robinson Crusoe*. That picture of his friend Greg carried as a shadow against the flaming fall day. His father rode hard, as always, and the boy had to smack Patches continually to keep abreast. It was a long ride to the bridge in Richmond and they had, of course, to go out of the direct way a little after crossing Stony Creek in order to stop at Ben Mopes's place.

The cooper's property lay off the main road a piece, on the left beyond a cluster of maples. A dilapidated sign indicated to the surgeon that he had correctly figured the barrelmaker's situation. Stephen Donlewis turned past the half-rotted signpost into a narrow, winding lane which soon led into a run-down barnyard. From inside the open door of the once red barn that was now streaked with faded pink and rotting gray came the ringing hammer of measured workmanship. Dr. Donlewis rode through the barnyard and pulled up his big bay horse.

"Halloo, there!" he called.

The man who came out in response was short and stumpy with thin gray hair fringing a round, apple-ruddy face; he might have been a jolly, easygoing fellow save that his eyes betrayed him—they were pinched and set in horridly granulating lids, and he blinked them nervously every other moment. The surgeon was impressive in his good traveling clothes: his fine black cape with the dark-gray lining, his new long black trousers that ran down clear into his boot tops, his black waistcoat and embroidered gray vest, his fine beaver hat, for which he had paid seven dollars! The barrelmaker gave a sort of deferential half bow.

"Yes, suh, can I sarve ye?"

"Are you Ben Mopes, the barrelmaker?"

"Aye."

"I've come in answer to your notice in the Richmond *Enquirer*," the doctor opened the proper subject immediately.

"About Jeb, eh? Where be he?"

"At my house. I'm a surgeon and the boy's bided with me, for he had broken his leg; I knew not until yesterday that he was indented; I shall have him back here tonight if you wish."

The man's beady eyes, set close above his pointed, overly ruddy nose, reminded Gregory of a snipe somehow. The fellow grinned, pleased, and his mouth was full of bad teeth, which made him even more unpleasant to look upon. "Aye, I want him; 'tis my busy season now and I reckon he well knows't!"

"Did you know he was hurt? Had he broken his leg before he went off? I supposed not. . . ." The doctor could not resist pumping the man, for the mystery of the boy still haunted him.

"He weren't broke-legged when he run off but I chased him on horse till it got dark; reckon he broke the leg somewheres on way," Mopes suggested, and the surgeon nodded.

The cooper eyed the doctor and his well-garbed son carefully. Greg thought he narrowed his beady eyes as he asked, "Ye did not read my first notice last May? Ye did not suspect the boy all these months? 'Tis a misdemeanor to harbor a runaway! I asked after him everywhere but I couldn' afford to advertise continual." The barrelmaker must have been considering how he might yet retain his twenty-five dollars' reward money, for he asked again. "Did ye not know that 'tis a misdemeanor to abet a runaway, suh?"

"Yes, I know!" Stephen Donlewis said. "Perhaps I should ask you, Mr. Mopes, why the boy became a runaway in the first place?"

"Should ye? I've not asked what manner of surgeon ye be, though I know it takes no four months to heal a broke leg!" the man responded boldly.

The growing altercation raised excitement like a ball in Gregory's throat; he pressed his tongue against the roof of his mouth.

"I found the boy with more than a broken leg," Stephen Donlewis retorted; his face became stern, for the cooper's words irritated him. "He was like to die of the infection from the cut on his shoulder!"

The cooper screwed up his mouth drolly. "Ah, that," he muttered.

"You knew of it?" the surgeon prodded.

" 'Tweren't a thing like to kill him less he let it go careless, runnin' off like that."

"Perhaps he did that, but he ought not to have been pushed to running off in such condition," the doctor remarked with acidy emphasis.

"Ef he says he were pushed to run off, he lies, for he were never beaten," Mr. Mopes began shouting, as though he were becoming anxious. "If I'm to argue gettin' my bonded boy back, doctor, I'm payin' no reward for't; and though I know not your name, I can find it out."

This was true enough, of course, for there were not many surgeons in Chesterfield County. However, the doctor informed the man immediately. "I am Stephen Donlewis of Fairville; and I agree that the lad was not beat." Greg thought his father was actually becoming conciliatory for a moment, for he continued, "I would know, though, out of professional curiosity, how he came to be cut so oddly upon the shoulder and once before, earlier, on the upper arm?"

"The boy is indentured to me; how I used him good or bad be my own affair, I be thinkin', but I'll be sayin' this much: he was stubborn and ornery and cowardly to boot!" Mopes spat out harshly.

The surgeon rolled in his underlip and gave no indication of how he received the cooper's opinion, but Greg burst out hotly, "He be not cowardly!"

His father tossed his head in his direction and gave him a telling look.

"I'm a barrelmaker, aye, and at the trade Jeb did fair and worked willing, mostly; but I'm also a bit of a showman and I make my winter's keep at court days and during spring and fall fairs, times like right now. And I tell ye, the boy be a coward and a disgrace to his father and mother! And 'twas his own fault he were cut because he'd not hold steady," Mr. Mopes said.

"That's a lie!" Gregory interrupted, shouting quite boldly again. "Bart was brave and steady enough when we set his leg!"

"Quiet, mind your manners," his father snapped at him, raising a threatening hand.

"Come along inside and I'll show ye!" Mopes invited.

The doctor looped his reins over his pommel; his mare would stand. Greg tied Patches to an old sawhorse in the yard.

The barn was musty and thick with sawdust. Barrel hoops hung overhead on long pegs, and piles of different-length staves littered the floor. The short man pushed his way past a line of barrels to a long bench on which lay many of his tools: hammers, saws, screw drivers, adzes. At one end of this bench was a long, narrow box. This the cooper opened carefully, revealing a dozen knives neatly arrayed on a velours lining; side by side they were placed, all exactly alike. Mopes picked up two of them and, turning, quick as a flash, tossed them half across the barn, placing them neatly on either side of the head of a man painted in black on a far wall. Suddenly Gregory, at the same moment perhaps as his father, realized that the painted form was not that of a man; it was neither tall nor broad enough.

"I tell ye he moved! And he'd no need because I'm steady, I am, and renowned throughout the country round! And mark ye, ef'n' he moved at an exhibition, 'twould be *my* reputation! I nailed straps to the wall, I did, to punish 'im, and it done no good at all; he were more scared, plain cowardish like I told ye."

Dr. Donlewis stood staring almost blankly at the shadowy outline on the wall; Gregory looked at it too. Was his father hearing, as he was, Bart that first night as he shrank into the hospital cot:

"Don't! Don't tie me! I'll hold still, I promise! I promise, Mr. Ben! Don't bind me!"

Gregory felt choked up. He turned to his father; he could see his father's anger growing as the barrelmaker continued:

"I found out what'd make him toe the line though, I did! I tied a rope under his arms and dipped him in the well and——"

"You what!" the surgeon cried. The good Lord knew he'd been punished himself severely enough as an apprentice, as what enterprising imp of a lad had not been—and deservingly—but to be hung in a well by a rope that might slip or break—— It was preposterous! Turning around swiftly, the surgeon noticed two things: Gregory's blanched face and a half-empty bottle of cheap rum standing beyond the exhibition knife case; perhaps there was good reason for the cooper's overruddy complexion.

"Gregory, await me outside with the horses," the doctor directed.

Greg obeyed quickly, glad to get away from the birdy eyes of the cooper. As he picked his way past the finished and half-finished barrels, Greg heard his father ask, "How much of his indenture had the boy served?" And then the answer came faintly to his ears as he went out into the yard, "Three and a half o' the nine years."

After that the conversation in the barn became a blur, though Greg untied Patches and walked him back as close as he dared to the barn door. Once he thought it was the cooper's voice that rose, more shrill than hoarse, possibly in anger; and another time it could have been his father's ironic snap, indicative also of aroused feeling. It was perhaps a full quarter hour later that the surgeon emerged from the barn; he picked his way through the mud, mounted his horse quickly, lifted the reins, and nodded Gregory ahead toward the lane.

"Well, 'tis done now," the surgeon muttered and said no more at all until they had clattered through the second portion of the long covered bridge from Mayo's Island toward the cluster of houses that was Richmond.

"Did you get the reward money?" Gregory asked then, wanting to know other things, thinking he might provoke some conversation.

But his father simply replied, "No."

"I—I was thinking—I couldn't help thinking about how Bart got back your gold needle," Greg offered next.

"Oh, be quiet!" His father snarled.

Gregory, properly silenced, trotted over the cobbled streets of the capital. The dark rain clouds of a sudden storm huddled overhead now, almost extinguishing the sunset. With the darkening sky, the coming dusk, and the disappointment of the interview at the cooper's, Gregory felt uneasy. He actually shivered a little. So he was glad it was warmish in the apothecary's shop. Greg waited patiently in the outer room, admiring the stores of materials. How Bart would enjoy a pharmacy like this one! Dr. Donlewis remained closeted in the rear for some time with the pharmacist, an elderly Scotsman.

A pretty set of pink-porcelain jars with myrrh, thyme, jalap, and other herbaceous and resinous substances attracted Gregory's attention; he was still admiring these when the two men came out. The apothecary nodded to Greg.

"And how are you, lad?" he asked. "Taking to the making of medicaments, eh?" This question only reminded Gregory that he had been doing less of that sort of thing than ever, due to the presence of Bart. As he muttered a polite affirmative, he felt his throat clogging at the thought of his friend's likely departure.

His father was gathering up two neatly tied bundles and setting them carefully into his saddlebags, which he had laid upon the apothecary's counter when he had first come in. "Well, John," he said to the Scotsman, "as long as you understand my plight, and how I got into it," this very softly.

"You don't suppose I'm really worried about you paying your bills, doctor?" the pharmacist smiled. He was a slight, acidy man with a bony face and thin, stark-white hair that showed his ruddy scalp clean and shining beneath. He had a heart-warming smile though and, unlike most men his age, rather good teeth, straight and white.

"I'd like to be able to say I wasn't worried about paying them," Stephen Donlewis answered; Gregory looked at the two men, puzzled. For after all, hadn't his father come for that purpose, to pay his bills? The surgeon continued, "You'll not condescend to see the boy?"

"I don't need anyone, Steve, though I've often envied you your many sons," the apothecary smiled again. "Now if my daughter had stayed to home in Richmond and brought me up a parcel of grandchildren—well, never mind that. Whenever you get around to coming back, that will be fine, sir."

Dr. Donlewis shook his head slightly. "You're no man to bargain with, John Stewart, so I'll say good day."

The pharmacist chuckled as though the doctor's remark were a kind of joke. Then he said "Good day" also, as Dr. Donlewis picked up the saddlebags and put a firm hand on Greg's shoulder and turned him toward the door.

"Get along, boy, or 'twill be full dark before we've crossed the river," the surgeon grumbled, fastening his heavy cape tight against the drizzle.

They outrode the storm, however, as they trotted briskly homeward along the Petersburg pike. The doctor remained taciturn, almost grim, as though the change in weather had embittered him the more; he spoke nothing until they turned into their very own driveway. There he dropped off his horse and called for Arne and then waved Gregory in by way of the kitchen.

"Set a place for me," the doctor called to his wife, who was mixing dumplings. Margaret looked surprised, since he rarely came to eat with the family, except Sundays. " 'S Keith in from Merryhaven? A storm's rumbling about up northwest."

"He came home an hour gone." Mistress Donlewis advised.

"Good," the surgeon's keen eye roved the big kitchen. Launa was setting the table, old Cora still browning the roast at the spit. Bart stood with his back turned at the doorway to the passage, his knapsack beside him, his hands thrust deep in his pockets, his thick hair neatly brushed; he looked taller in the neat blue serge with the dark-blue corduroy jacket. "Well, we've yet a two-hundred-dollar bill with John Stewart," Stephen Donlewis observed to his wife, who stared at him as if he had lost his sense. Then unbuttoning his riding cape and speaking as he walked through the huge kitchen, he said, "I suppose I've been in worse shape monetarily, but not much worse. You, boy!' Then he flicked his left hand at Bart. "Get out of those fine clothes and build me a fire in the pharmacy basin, one that will develop properly into coals during supper. You'll really work for your keep now, and I'll thank you not to fret!"

Gregory stood staring, drop-jawed but not any more astonished than poor Bart, who shook beneath the surgeon's harsh voice and frowning mien.

"Steve, what is it?" Mistress Donlewis asked anxiously, handing the dumpling batter to Cora. "I thought you were going to Richmond to pay John Stewart's account."

"Yes, but things have turned out differently."

Keith came in from the passage. "What of it all, Father?" he asked eagerly. "What about Bart and the cooper?"

"This!" the doctor took a paper from his breast pocket and thrust it under his son's nose.

As Keith read aloud, the surgeon met his wife's eyes and Bart stood, shaken, swallowing copiously, overwhelmed; he had gritted his teeth all day against a return to the knife throwing.

"That barrelmaker, Meg, was impossible!" Stephen Donlewis stated with his gun-gray eyes snapping.

"Why, you've taken over Bart's indenture, haven't you?" Keith announced. "You hear that, Bart?" he turned to the astonished boy. "Father's taken your papers!"

"Yes, and the transaction must be recorded next week at Petersburg, I believe; you can probably ride down for me, Keith. I did it because I thought that cooper unworthy of any apprentice and—well, I thought I could talk that lonely old Stewart into trying the boy against my medicines bill. But that miserly Scotsman is tighter than a new pair of garters and would have nothing to do with the very idea! So," the surgeon explained.

Everyone stood silent a moment in complete surprise; poor Bart gulped harder. Then he blurted out, "I—I can't stay here like that, sir—thank ye kindly, but I can't be beholdin' like that; I'll go back to Ben Mopes." He reached a hand toward Keith and the contract as though he would take it upon himself to return it to the barrel-maker.

"You'll do nothing of the kind. I've bought you, fair and square, and you've me to serve. You'll do as I say and since I have said, be about my business!" the surgeon fairly shouted as he snatched the indenture from Keith and out of Bart's reach and folded it neatly to thrust back into his waistcoat.

Bart covered his face with both hands and his shoulders heaved. Gregory coughed hard, for he had never seen his friend give way to his feelings thus. Perhaps the doctor's glare softened slightly.

"Was I wrong, Jebart Worrell," the surgeon inquired, "to suppose that you had a real interest in the compounding of medicament?"

The boy opened his fingers to look at this new master. "No, suh," he whispered, "I—I've dreamed on makin' medicines. . . ."

The doctor smiled at long last. "Well, off with you then and be about the rudiments wi' me . . . make my fire so that you do not keep us at suppertime!"

XV.

A Rather Sad Story

AFTER supper, Dr. Donlewis sent for Gregory in his study.

"I know that I should have talked to you on our way home, Greg," the surgeon began, "but 'twas too nasty for most of the ride." He looked ruefully at the rain as though he resented its following him to his own house. "Then, too, I couldn't bring myself to speak about it because I had thought Stewart would take Bart, at least on several months' trial against my account. Otherwise I'd not have taken the indenture so quickly. You may as well be told now that we are pressed for money. I may have to borrow from your Uncle Philip against my fees at Merryhaven for the rest of this year in order to send Keith to Williamsburg. Do not speak of all this to Bart, however, for I fear that I have said too much already."

Gregory nodded. "Bart knows what you have given out for him and I think he feels that you believe him ungrateful."

"Nonsense! What sort of friend are you to him if you allow him to believe that? Rather you should continually beat on him and plague him to study and improve himself. I think Mr. Stewart may yet take an interest in training him as an assistant, but he's a cagey, cautious old buzzard and I spoiled Bart's immediate chances when I was honest enough to say that he was unschooled. Well, you help him all you can, Greg, you hear—and oh, yes! one thing more: get him to talk about his folks. Stewart asked me his background and I could tell him nothing. And *I* shan't go back to that Mopes again."

"Yes, sir, Father, I'll see what I can do and find out," Gregory promised, though he was remembering how tight-lipped Bart had been from the very beginning.

His father dismissed him. "Go to your own studies now."

As Gregory left the surgery, he noticed that his bedroom door was shut. He opened it deliberately. Sure enough, Bart was there, lying tensely on his side of the big bed with his palms pressed against his temples. His body heaved irregularly.

"What's the matter, Bart?" Greg asked. "Don't you want to stay with us? I thought you'd be happy about it."

Bart turned to him and then sat up. He rubbed at his eyes with the backs of his fists. "Nothing's the matter, Greg, really. It's just that I can't repay your father for nothin' and he's done so much for me———"

"Can't repay him for anything," Greg corrected rather severely.

"Well, can't!" Bart muttered.

"You needn't repay him because he'll make you work to redeem your indenture, never fear," the surgeon's son said, grinning.

Bart met his look and had to smile. "I guess that's right!"

"But your father didn't want to keep my papers, Gregory," Bart said in a moment. "He expected the pharmacist in Richmond to take me as an apprentice and I could tell he was annoyed when it didn't work out———"

"He wasn't annoyed———" Gregory began.

"Oh yes, he was—I been around some, Greg; I know what 'tis to have an extra mouth to feed in hard times!" Bart stated.

133

"He'll make you work!" Greg repeated. "And he wants me to help you with your reading and writing and ciphering. So get your slate and I'll give you some problems to do and then you can write a composition while I do my Greek."

"What's a composition?" Bart wanted to know.

"A piece of writing that you make up yourself, you know."

"Don't know," Bart insisted.

"Well, just write something about what happened to you or describe some place or some person. You could describe someone, couldn't you? My father, for example, or your mother, maybe; do you remember your mother?"

Bart nodded and his whole face softened. Greg took the slate Bart fished out of a drawer and set four problems on it in his fine, neat figures. Then he went to get a bigger lantern from the kitchen.

When Gregory returned, Bart was biting on his left thumbnail and already working the second problem. He was good at problems and calculations, but a few scrawling lines for the composition took him a long time.

Looking over the piece of writing, at length, Greg wanted to laugh at the spelling and construction, but he couldn't because of what his friend had revealed.

The mothr of Jebart Worrell

I rimembr my mothr coaming her silklike brown hayr. She had a flowr fase marked by 2 vilet jools hr eyes and hr hayr was soft and foamy with shinny waves int. My mothr was smart and cud sing and act in the theaytr. She boar the name of Jessica and my fathr was Bartholomew so I got to be named out of both names Je for Jessica and Bart for Bartholomew. My mothr died too yung fr sech a ladee.

yr umble sarvint Jebart Worrell

Bart studied Greg's face anxiously as the surgeon's son read the large, even writing. Bart wrote slowly and painstakingly but neatly.

"You don't spell very well," Greg admitted, "but then I've noticed that even books don't always agree on spellings. I'll copy over what you have said, Bart, and show you how you can say it smoother."

Bart nodded in gratitude.

"Was your mother in the theater, really, the real theater?" Greg threw himself across the bed on his stomach and propped his head in his hands in the hope of drawing Bart out.

"Uh-huh, and my father too! My mother acted with my father—you know, they were together in it; that is, he played the hero and she was his lady fair. They were in the theater in New York and Phillydelphy and Petersburg, and Richmond, too, just everywhere. This was when I was very small. Then my father was killed one stormy winter night when a coach overturned. I don't know where it was. It was hard for my mother after that and she got sick a lot. We traveled about with a small company of show people and got into market days and court days and fairs, things like that, same as Mr. Mopes do," Bart explained, lying across the bed on his stomach, too, beside his friend. "My mother didn't like this as much as the real theater because she told me about how it was with my father . . . when she put me to bed at night, she told me some of the stories of the big plays she was in . . . she taught me my letters then, too, and to count. The small company was the best she could do without my father. I danced some myself back then when I was seven or eight, and I took care of the animals. We generally had some mules and a goat and chickens and ducks that we took about with us against starvin'. The fellow that ran the outfit, a Mr. Jenney, was pretty nice to my mother at first but he didn't like it afterwards when she got sicker and coughed all the time and fainted a lot. She had the lung fever, you know. . . ."

Greg nodded wisely. "Consumption; you can't cure it."

Bart choked up. "No, you can't! My—my mother died one Christmas time; I remember it well. We were in Frederick, Maryland, and Mr. Jenney come—I mean came—in and asked her just before where—where she wanted to be buried; I screamed and screamed because I knew what it meant— I can almost hear myself yet! But my mother didn't even cry; she just said, 'Be a good boy for Mr. Jenney, Jebart' . . . that was all. So she *is* buried in Frederick and I always wanted to go back there. In fact, I figured I was runnin' that way when I went from Mopes and broke my leg. . . . Well, Mr. Jenney kept talkin' about how it took him a lot of money to have arranged for my mother in a churchyard in Frederick; he kept on talkin' as how I weren't worth my keep. So about a year later he sold me to Mr. Mopes when we were down this way for the spring fairs. That's my whole story, Greg; reckon there was no point in keepin' it to myself any longer. Anyhow, you can explain to the doctor that I was from decent folk and not thieves or anything like that——"

"Bart, don't you know where any of your folks are? Didn't your mother or father talk about their relatives so's you could have gone to them instead of staying with that Mr. Jenney?" Greg wondered.

"My father had no folks, I reckon, 'ceptin' maybe 'way back in England, and my mother never went to see anybody that I can remember. She was born in Virginia though, I know she told me that."

"Now that's a good thing to know because old John Stewart would be likely to think better of you if you could say your mother was born in this state—his family goes back in Richmond to when the town was started!"

Gregory said. "And, Bart—we never thought you were from bad folk!"

"No tellin' what your father thought," Bart said. "It's good to speak out though, makes you feel easier inside . . . though I'm not much easier 'cause I like not to be beholdin' to your father, Gregory; knowing I am sits on my chest like a lump of lead because Mr. Jenney was in debt for me, too. . . ."

"Maybe he was and maybe not," Gregory put in shrewdly. "It's altogether different with us, Bart. You've worked willing for my father and he knows that you have. We're not rich, as you once thought, but we're not poor either. And, Bart, you know that I always liked you, even when you were stubborn and secretive and afraid; but you also know well that my father did not, that he was harsh and suspicious; yet now Father has given his bond for you! From my father such a thing is more than simple kindness and concern; he marks you, I think, worthy of his hope."

"I pray God I be worthy of it then!" Bart whispered.

XVI.

Distilling Mischief

THE next week Greg was especially busy with schoolwork. About the only time Bart saw him was when they worked on reading and ciphering before bedtime. The surgeon kept his new bound boy occupied, too, as handy jack in the surgery, chief errand boy and, as before, in the pharmacy. Bart was now thoroughly familiar in the apothecary room, although there were items he was forbidden to touch, pain-easers and sleep-producers and drugs that could burn or poison upon contact. The one thing the doctor seemed to use least was ether. He kept only a very small bottle of it and Bart was quite surprised one afternoon when Greg came seeking it.

Bart followed the surgeon's son curiously to the carved-oak railing of the surgery to see how the drug was to be employed. Dr. Donlewis took court plaster from a man's back with it and afterward ordered Gregory to put the bottle away and dispose of the cloth he had used. Bart scuttled back to the prescriptions he was bottling.

"My, that ether has a strong smell, hasn't it?" Bart observed as Gregory put the bottle into its accustomed place, laying the saturated cloth on the marble countertop a moment.

"Yes." Greg answered short as if he didn't want to talk.

"Your father will need some more soon," Bart remarked.

Greg agreed. "He'll make it when he does. It's not hard to make—you use sulphuric acid and distill it; you've seen us use the distilling apparatus?"

His friend nodded.

"My father doesn't keep much ether about," Greg added as he measured with his thumb and reckoned that there would be scarcely enough for another such use as his father had just made of the stuff.

"Is't poison?" Bart inquired.

"Yes, and——"

Right at that moment Tullah called in. "Massa Greg, your pony saddled and waitin' for you to get along with that medicine for Mistress Bunker!"

"Odysseus! I was to have delivered it before that last patient came!" Greg grabbed at a package on the countertop and took himself off, forgetting the ether-saturated rag that he had laid upon the marble compounding slab.

Bart sniffed at the acrid odor and then opened the small square window over the pharmacy basin. He wasn't sure whether he ought soak the cloth, burn it, or throw it away, so he waited. A bit later, finished with his bottles, he set them away and went into the surgery with a napkin full of clean instruments, which he distributed in their proper places. The surgeon was standing at the rail between surgery and waiting room, talking with a leather-faced farmer about an operation. Presently he dismissed the man and nodded Bart after him into the pharmacy. They had just stepped within the narrow room when Gregory came running up the waiting-room steps. He had not got fully across the door sill before his father literally bellowed his name! Greg, blanching a little at the harsh tone, scurried to the pharmacy. The moment he stepped within range of his father, the doctor cuffed him so fiercely that he recoiled against the shelves behind him. Bart gasped in surprise.

"What have I told you about ether? Burn that cloth and then answer why you did not do so immediately!" the surgeon cried.

Gregory hastily caught up the rag, which really smelled but faintly now in the fresh breeze from the window. He threw it in the grate in the iron basin of the pharmacy, where a small, hot fire burned. It puffed into flame immediately with a popping report and sizzled merrily.

"Well?" the doctor's voice still blasted and Greg trembled.

"I—I forgot it—truly I did. Tullah called about Patches being ready and I hurried off to Bunker's. I—I had forgot that too, sir," Gregory confessed, white-faced save where his father's hand had reddened his cheek.

"You'll make a fine surgeon with your woolgathering! Go to your room and to bed!" the doctor commanded, and he clapped his son stingingly upon the shoulder. Then he whirled upon Bart. "And *you!* Offer him no solace. . . ."

Though "solace" was a new word to the lad, he gathered very readily what it meant. His supper stuck in his throat afterward, but he begged no sympathy for Greg and made no pleas. Keith asked about his brother, noting his absence from the table.

"Greg's displeased your father," Margaret Donlewis explained briefly and Bart was grateful that he did not have to tell the whole tale.

But afterward Keith snatched at Bart's sleeve in the passage and pulled him into the dark sewing room. "What's he done, what's Greg done?" the older Donlewis wanted to know.

"He forgot to put away a cloth with a chemical on it—ether, 'twas," Bart told him.

"Oh, ether!" Keith nodded wisely and asked no more, which pricked Bart's already full measure of curiosity the more.

Bart had saved a tart and a bit of cornbread from his supper, and he put these away carefully in his compartment while he filled two more prescriptions for the doctor and delivered them. No late patients came; at half after nine Bart was finished in the pharmacy and free to go to bed if he chose. He went into the bedchamber with a stub of candle, which he lighted carefully. Greg was not asleep; he blinked at the candlelight and then sat up and rubbed his fingers through his thick black curls.

"Is it all right to talk?" Bart whispered.

"Father didn't say you nay, did he?" Gregory asked.

"No."

"Good, I'm glad," Greg said.

"I brought you something to eat," Bart unwrapped the

140

now crumby contribution. "Remember all the times you brought me things?"

Greg wolfed the food. His jaw hurt a little when he ate—deuced if his father didn't have a hard hand!

"Greg," Bart asked, "why was your father so angry? It seemed a little thing——"

"It isn't a little thing—to him. 'Tis a long story. My brother Guy, who was a surgeon too—well, just last year he—he died from—ether. We're not sure exactly what happened, but he had been doing some experiments. Long ago, when he was a boy like me, he burned his hand badly; my father, treating it, used a combination of ether and opium, something he had seen done once in England. Guy felt much less pain, and later, when he was studying at Edinburgh University himself, Guy read some things which indicated that others had noticed that ether could put you unaware—besides, the medical students fooled with it a good deal, with it and nitrous oxide—so Guy began to study the effects of both drugs. He kept careful notes and only used small amounts, which he increased bit by bit; he did go unconscious to a degree a few times —not for long, a minute, two, four minutes—then one day——" the boy choked up, turned into his pillow.

Bart sat stiff with a boy's sympathy that he could not put into words. He waited tensely until Greg lifted his face.

"I found him," Gregory whispered at length. "You see, I used to go over to watch him in his surgery in Everton. My father thinks the bottle tipped upon the handkerchief he had folded over his face. His wife, Guy's wife, thought he was out on a call and when I came from school—'twas too late. . . . My father will not tolerate the idea of any-one's experimenting with ether; he wouldn't let me have Guy's notes but I copied them off without his knowing, before Guy's wife took all his things with her to Canada."

" 'Tis an awful story," Bart commented. "I don't blame your father."

"Well, I think he's wrong!" Greg blazed boldly. "Someday I will do what Guy did because I believe in his idea. He was careful—it was an accident that he died, just a terrible accident—I'm not afraid of the ether at all!"

Bart stared. "You ain't? A bit?"

"No, but I know you must be careful—don't misunderstand that! Maybe someday—with you to help me——"

"You think we could go on and find out somethin'?" The eternal excitement of quest poured from the enthusiastic Greg into Bart and shone in his bright blue eyes.

"Yes." Gregory swiped a hand across his face.

"You talk like I'll get to stay on with you always. . . ." Bart murmured.

"Well, naught's been said about your leaving. Father's not even mentioned Mr. Stewart lately," Greg observed.

Bart nodded.

"If—if I get a chance tomorrow, I'll look up Guy's notes and show them to you and see what you think," Greg promised. "Now we'd better be quiet before he hears us in there. . . ." he nodded surgeryward, grinning.

Bart peeled off his clothes and pulled his shift on over his head and crawled into bed.

Gregory kept his word and hauled out the notebook he had copied off from his brother's. The terse descriptions of the young surgeon's experiments in apothecary terms were not too hard for Bart to read. Both boys pored over them clandestinely, every chance they got in the next few days. Then Gregory plotted; his father still went to the plantations on Wednesdays and frequently now it was full dark before he got back. If Greg hurried from school, he might, on such a day, have a couple of hours before his father's arrival. It would depend on whether there were patients waiting.

The following Wednesday, as luck had it, no one came all afternoon, and Bart had the distilling apparatus out and ready when Gregory arrived. Bart measured off the alcohol and vitriol carefully, according to the specifications of the formula Greg had printed out. The two lads shut themselves in the pharmacy room with the door locked, but this was not so unusual a procedure as to cause any suspicion among the various members of the doctor's household, for Dr. Donlewis himself often worked with the pharmacy door latched, not wanting to be disturbed for minor matters. Gregory took deliberate and necessary caution and worked slowly. When they had drawn off the liquid ether, Bart took the apparatus apart and cleaned it and set it away. Gregory hid their stoppered bottle and tidied up.

"Now if we want to start experimenting, we're all ready," the surgeon's son observed, pleased with himself.

It was suppertime and the doctor had not come. The boys went to table with no more thought of what they'd been doing. Evidently the surgeon tethered his horse at the drive gate, intending to go out later, for no one heard his horse. His voice sundered a quiet moment when everyone was enjoying Margaret Donlewis's apple pudding. It was Gregory that he called, and the boy dropped his spoon into his bowl and flew toward the passage. His father stood grim before the hearth in the waiting room.

"How often have you dared flout me, boy?" the doctor demanded, level and low.

Gregory trembled. "How d'ye mean, s—sir?" he stammered.

"Haven't I forbid you to touch the ether?"

"Yes, sir, and I've not disobeyed you———" He ran

143

that out glibly, for he had thought up that it was technically true; he had made his own ether.

Dr. Donlewis was too sharp in the ways of boys; he'd had enough sons and students! "No, you made your own, eh?" He beckoned his son after him as he turned into the apothecary room. Ducking his head under the counter, the surgeon pulled out the bottle Gregory had hidden in his compartment. The two boys had forgotten the lingering pervasiveness of the drug they had made; there had been some minor spillage during the bottling process and the odor had led the keen surgeon into easy recognition of what had taken place. "You know very well why you've been forbidden the stuff?" the doctor asked.

"We—we need some," Gregory floundered; he had thought that up, too, during the anxieties of his secret operation.

"That's not why you made it and then hid it away! I stand surprised that you would dishonor your name with such prevarication," his father returned sharply.

By this time Bart had come meekly from the supper table and stood hesitant in the waiting room. Gregory dropped his head in shame; his face flamed; he knotted his fingers.

"Did you not purpose to use it yourself?" the surgeon pursued.

"Yes, sir," he admitted then.

"Ah! I can guess for what reason," Stephen Donlewis stooped again and came up with the notebook Greg had so painstakingly copied off the year before. "Is this not writ in your hand?"

"Yes, sir."

"I'd no notion you copied off these notes of Guy's for the first thing, and I'll not be disobeyed in any matter. Go cut you a switch, boy, and send in Tullah, since you must be whipped so you remember!" The doctor felt in his pocket for his barlow knife, handed it to his son, stepped into the waiting room and tossed the objectionable notebook into the just-lit fire in the hearth. Then he strode into his study, leaving the door ajar.

Gregory went outside, looking neither to left nor right; in all probability he did not see Bart huddled against one of the big waiting-room chairs. Bart watched Gregory head toward a clump of young birches beside the brook until the dusk swallowed his figure up. Then Bart darted over to the fireplace and snatched out the notebook that had just begun to burn around its edges. He flipped it out upon the hearthstones and stamped out the fire. Looking about quickly and stealthily for a hiding place, he noticed the doctor's pottery umbrella stand, into which he stuffed the notebook. He blew the scattered cinder shreds back into the fire pit. Then, bolstering all his courage with a deep breath, he went to stand upon the threshold of the doctor's study, into which sacred precinct he had never ventured unbidden.

"Yes?" the surgeon's sharp tone closed Bart's throat and he swallowed painfully before he could speak.

" 'Tis me you should whip," he got out at last. " 'Twas on my account Greg distilled the ether, for I prodded him to't."

"Did you so?" Stephen Donlewis leaned his left arm upon his desk and looked levelly at the lad.

"Yessir, and I ain't wantin' him takin' my due again since he were caned fer me once!" Bart breathed short as though his fustian vest had suddenly become too tight for him; his voice went hoarse and his old speech came out again. "Suh, 'twas the story of Guy that got to me and I—I wanted fer Greg to do somethin' because I wanted to help him—I wanted to do somethin' really *big* fer 'im——"

"Such as getting him birched?" the doctor suggested, turning down his mouth sourly.

"No, suh," Bart muttered, looking floorward.

"Hear me!" the doctor said emphatically. "I should have sent you packing long ago save what you've done for Gregory. You've not seen, have you? You've never considered why I took your papers and have retained you when I could ill afford it? Know you not that Greg stands almost on a par with the two students who are ready to enter medical school? Think you he'd have got so far if he'd been washing all my bottles, rolling all my pills, running all my errands?" The doctor smiled his rare smile for a brief moment. "Serve where you may, young man, and how you may. Don't you think I know why Gregory attempted that tooth pulling the other day? Perhaps you are better for my son right now than all my books, Bart.

"Furthermore, let me correct you; 'tis Gregory I shall have whipped! It was he whom I cautioned against the ether. If he has not the courage to stand against coaxing or any other pressure, he is unworthy of my time. Implicit obedience, boy, is the right of a master and the duty of an apprentice and my son shall not forget this! You will bear witness to his learning the lesson." The doctor rose and came around the side of his desk; he caught at Bart's arm and steered him into the waiting room.

Tullah had come in with Gregory behind him, in time for the surgeon's last words. The boy handed the goodly birch switch he had cut into the servant's hand.

"Over the rail, not sparingly!" the surgeon ordered firmly. But then he stopped the punishment after four whacks, making it more a token warning. He shook Bart unexpectedly and directed Gregory to scour the apothecary basins.

Conscience-stricken over his part in Greg's defection,

Bart could not venture to help and so provoke the surgeon's undoubted displeasure. He did stand about for the chance to retrieve the charred notebook from the umbrella stand and smuggled it into their bedroom. Gregory burst into tears at its receipt and hid it in a far corner of his clothespress. Neither lad had any courage to discuss their escapade when they prepared for bed that night, and Tawny sat lop-eared at their silence.

XVII.

Failure in Richmond

Two major operations on well-to-do planters who paid their fees immediately plus the bimonthly plantation money netted the doctor a small purse by the middle of the month. He decided immediately to send fifty dollars to John Stewart before it became necessary to dispense any more on behalf of Keith's college. Therefore he called Gregory and Bart into his study as soon as Greg got home from school on Saturday the nineteenth.

"I want you both to ride to Richmond to pay Mr. Stewart against my account," the surgeon explained. "Bart, I want him to get a look at you; now make sure that you are polite and make a good impression. If he asks you any questions, answer nicely, as well as you can. He's a good, fair man, though a bit crusty. If he ever does condescend to take you as his apprentice, you can be assured of a fine future, understand?"

"Yes, sir, I'll be seemly," Bart promised. "I—I wish you didn't owe so much on my part, sir."

"That is entirely beside the point! Stewart knows me

well enough to be certain I shall pay my debt. 'Tis for your acceptance that I must keep prodding him, for I cannot afford to offer you anything like the pharmaceutical opportunities that he can," the surgeon smiled, but in his stern manner, which was never much comfort to the boys.

Two or three times en route to the capital Bart brought up the pharmacy bill and Gregory knew it worried the lad.

"Greg, I have my pin with me," Bart said finally. "Do you think it is of some value?"

"Let's stop under that tree a minute to rest," Greg suggested, for they had been riding hard. "We can look at it together carefully."

Bart took out his only treasure. The two boys counted the jewels: twelve pearls made up the *J* and then there were four red, three blue, and two green stones. Gregory could not guess at the value of the piece.

"Why are you concerned?" he asked.

Bart explained that though he hated the idea of giving up the keepsake, he had thought of offering it to the apothecary against Dr. Donlewis's account.

"I suppose you could ask," Greg said, "but Father's not been pushing you on account of his debt—he even said you were worth more to him than he paid out—and besides, Mr. Stewart's not been pushing Father."

"I know, Gregory, but 'tis how I feel inside of me that's pushing me!"

"Oh!" Greg looked at him with better understanding as Bart folded the piece of jewelry away.

They pulled their ponies out of a grass patch and went on their way. At the pharmacist's they had to wait while Mr. Stewart finished a prescription for an old gentleman. Then Gregory tendered the purse his father had sent. The pharmacist counted out the money on his long table and read the short note the surgeon had in-

148

cluded with it. Painstakingly he made a receipt in Dr. Donlewis's name and returned this to Gregory with the empty pocketbook. He pushed his narrow spectacles up on his nose and looked keenly at Bart, who was wearing his best clothes and one of Keith's school tricornes.

"So you're the fellow Steve Donlewis would palm off on me?" the old Scotsman asked. "What's your name now—Worrell, eh?"

"Yes, sir, Jebart Worrell."

"You like to work wi' medicines and chemicals, eh? Not many boys would."

"Yes, I do, sir, and the doctor has taught me a lot. I'm strong, too——"

"I can observe things for m'sel', boy!" Stewart snapped. "And I know somewhat aboot ye, that you worked for the cooper Mopes and was mistreated."

Bart started to shake his head.

"If Steve Donlewis says you was mistreated, so you were," Stewart insisted.

Gulping, the boy blurted hopefully, "If ye'd but try me, suh, I could sarve yuh well." His old speech leaked out under his tension.

"You think so, eh?" Stewart scratched at his left cheek hard.

"Yes, suh," for a moment Bart hoped he had made the good impression the doctor had wanted; then his castle of dreams clattered about his ears.

"Well, I be not wantin' anyone, understand? Now be off with you before it darkens along your way, both of you—off, off!" the apothecary waved a hand in dismissal.

Bart turned toward the door with Greg; then he pivoted and came back to the wooden counter. "Mr. Stewart, suh, I've naught in the world but this. I want to give it you against the doctor's account because I know he can ill afford to save up that much money in these times." He pulled out the handkerchief in which he had folded his pin.

"Did I ask for a settlement of Steve Donlewis's account?" Stewart shouted across to the boy.

"No, suh, but it's on account o' me he has't." Bart laid the piece of jewelry on the countertop. "If 'tis of any value at all, suh——"

"Did the doctor tell ye to wheedle me thus, boy?" Stewart glared at Bart fiercely, his cheeks pinking.

"No, suh, he did not!" Bart cried.

John Stewart looked down then at the pin hard through his spectacles. Then he snatched it up and held it beneath a swinging lantern. He was quite old, the boys could see, for his hands shook. "Where'd you get a thing like this, boy?" the pharmacist demanded. "D'ye steal it mayhap?"

"No, sir, I don't steal!" Bart stated pridefully. " 'Tis rightly mine and if you believe it has value, I'll give it you."

"I don't want it—or your service! Get out, the two of you!" the old gentleman roared at them and flung the pin down. Then he spun about and stood hunch-shouldered with his chin folded into his stock; he did not look at the boys again as they tiptoed out.

Before mounting Keith's pony, Bart wrapped his pin back carefully in the kerchief and put it deep in his shirt pocket. Later, as the two boys clomped through the covered bridges over the James River, Bart observed, "That's just how I felt when he threw down my pin, everything rattling over my head! You'd think the roof was going to fall down on us, wouldn't you?"

Gregory laughed. " 'Tis that big wagon coming in behind."

"Well, the roof's fallen in wi' me and Mr. Stewart, don't you think?" Bart asked wryly.

Gregory just shrugged as though he were not convinced. "I don't know; Father's very persistent, you know. And Bart, your pin must have some value, for did you notice how Mr. Stewart examined it under the light and then asked if you stole it?"

It was Bart's turn to shrug as he settled himself to the pony's gait on the open road beyond the bridge. He allowed himself most of the way home to worry over what his present master would think of their whole adventure. Should they tell the surgeon about the pin? Finally Bart asked Greg's opinion. They decided not to mention the piece of jewelry but just to tell the part about Mr. Stewart's bellowing that he didn't want anyone's services.

Dr. Donlewis, as Greg had predicted, simply stated that he would keep sending Bart to Stewart from time to time to see if his attitude would soften.

XVIII.

Greg on His Own

THE following Wednesday Dr. Donlewis accepted an offer from his brother to share a ride to Fredericksburg in the comfortable Merryhaven coach, which boasted good springs, coachmen and postriders. Stephen Donlewis had long promised to operate upon the harelip of a cobbler's son in Fredericksburg; he had had some past success with the difficult and delicate operation. This chance seemed opportune. He would leave early Thursday and return sometime on Saturday.

"Since no one is in the hospital and I've no serious

cases on the plantations, I should go while I can," the surgeon told Gregory. "You will see any who come, evenings after school. You should have no trouble with minor things. Should someone come with severe abdominal pain, put him to bed here and pray. I might do more; you must not! Otherwise I can trust to your judgment in an emergency?"

"I'll do my best, sir," Greg promised.

The bustle of preparation in the morning for the doctor's departure was repeated in the afternoon. Keith was going to Williamsburg early on the morrow to take some of his boxes and make the final arrangements for his lodging. With this turmoil the day ran out quickly into a rather sultry evening for October, portentous of storm. Malcolm came up for supper and with an amusing show of importance sat in his father's place at table.

"And Dr. Donlewis, how do you do tonight?" he teased Gregory, who giggled and stated that business was slow.

A high wind rose just past midnight. Gregory woke at the echoing clamor of the small shutter banging in the apothecary room. Bart slept deeply on his side of the bed. Accompanied by Tawny, whom he had pushed unceremoniously off the bed, Greg pattered through the surgery barefoot and hooked the offending shutter fastener. The moon, a dented piece of silver crossbarred with scuttling streamers of dark cloud, had risen above the barn. It might rain, Greg thought, for even as he looked out, the last cloud streamer widened into a mounting curtain of blackness. Sure enough, he just got back into bed with his feet tucked against Tawny's warm belly when a handful of rain was flung violently upon the housetop. The boy lay listening. Finally he lifted himself on an elbow to blow out the stub of candle he had lighted; he was arrested in this act by hammering on the waiting-room door.

Tullah, sleeping in the surgery on the couch as a safe-guard during the doctor's absence, woke at the knocking, though, like Bart, he had slept through the shutter noises and Gregory's passage. He came to the back-chamber door where Greg stood now with his candle in hand. Tullah had the flint gun with him and he backed down the surgery steps to light the nearest lantern.

"Better put on clothes, boy; mighty sick-lookin' man they bringin' out of a wagon," the colored man advised, and he snatched his bedding from the top of the couch and stuffed it handily away behind the passage door.

Gregory retreated into his bedroom and tore into shirt and leather breeches. He thrust his bare toes into moccasins. Then he shook Bart.

"Wake up, I might need you, get up!" he warned.

Going down into the surgery, he buttoned his sleeves above his elbows as he had so often seen his father do upon the reception of a patient. Two tall but stoop-shouldered farm lads carried in an older man, whom they laid upon the couch. His blue field trousers were soaked an unrecognizable muddy color from profuse bleeding.

"His eyesight ain't good and he stumbled in the barn and fell upon a scythe blade. He done bled an awful lot; where's the doctor?" one lad asked.

"My father's gone off," Gregory explained.

"For the night?"

"For two; he's gone to Fredericksburg to do an operation and is not to get back afore Saturday night," Greg was straightforward.

"Oh, my good Lord!" one farm boy cried and the other explained, "My father daren't be moved much more; he's fainted and fainted account o' he lost a lot o' blood before we ever found him; we're from 'way below

Court House; we thought your father'd be better'n anyone else!"

"Let me look," Gregory offered. He took a shears
from his father's small cabinet and carefully cut away
the soiled, torn right trouser leg. "The tourniquet's too
tight; have you been releasing it?"

"No, ye can't! 'Tis a big bleeder he's cut; it squirts
out o't, the blood!" one of the man's sons cried.

"No matter, the leg will die if you keep it cut off like
that, dry," Gregory stated. "I can fix a proper tourniquet and tend it—but it should not wait so long, the
wound—until my father returns. . . ."

The heavier-set and probably the elder of the two
regarded him carefully, remarking that he seemed to
know what he was talking about and also that his
fine hands touching the wound were steady. "Can you
do what must be done? Sew it or whatever? 'Tis no night
to be riding miles with someone in his condition to find
another surgeon!" the farmer's son said.

Mistress Donlewis, roused by Tullah, had come to
stand upon the surgery steps. Bart was already in the
surgery and had begun to lay out lint and bandaging.
Gregory looked over at his mother, worry starting to
crease his forehead.

"Can you, Greg?" Margaret whispered. "Can you do
what is requisite?"

He replied thickly, as tension began pulling at his
stomach. "I know how—I know how to ligate the artery
and suture the cut—but he must stay, afterward, for
Father to see. . . ."

The young men nodded in agreement with that. The
old man was moaning now and breathing hoarsely; one
of his sons knelt to hold his hands from the wound.
Gregory had already run a strand of the wool knit his
father had made especially for tourniquets above the

154

poor whipcord stricture and twisted a piece of narrow splint through the knot. He cut away the binding cord and the blood spurted from the artery. The man's son started, but Gregory controlled the bleeding quickly with a slight turn of his hand and watched the supplementary circulation flow down into the area that had been constricted. He wondered how long such circulation had been arrested and what serious effects such a thing might have, for there could be dangerous consequences, he knew.

"I'll help you, however you wish," Bart volunteered, noticing Greg's tight face. He reached up and caught at a lantern that was smoking and turned down the wick.

"Get me two basins of warm water and some clean cloth; most everything else is here in the cabinet. I'll want the Martell brandy—and a two-grain opium tablet from the stubby white jar on the top right shelf; you know the jar, Bart, but perhaps you'd better bring it to me anyway," Gregory directed. His voice was firm, almost vibrant like his father's, and Bart smiled encouragingly at him. "You can do this while I set up what is necessary," Greg went on to the farmer's second son, and he showed the fellow how to tighten and release the tourniquet.

Carefully Gregory set up his sutures in two separate needles to save time rethreading later; he selected a good silk ligature. He gave the man the sedative pill and a good-sized glass of brandy, on which the poor old fellow choked a little. Finally Greg got some old pieces of quilting and laid them as padding beneath the bad leg. He was ready. Bart stood by to hand things; the farmer's sons secured their father against violent jerking. Noticing her son's calm, Mistress Donlewis went into the kitchen to make some hot chocolate to serve after the work was done and before the young men's departure.

So far Gregory had been quite serene, efficient and

nerveless, but when the farmer cried out loudly during the ligation, Greg ground his teeth against listening and went on stolidly. He could feel his heart starting to pound in the old excitement; all too quickly it seemed as though his chest were going to burst. His ears rang, the hot, sick feeling came up inside him; his head began to ache. He wet his lips nervously and finally he gave Bart a quick, frantic look. He was putting in the stitches as his father had said, each one individually; he knew that his hands shook a little and that he was running his needle alternately too shallow or too deep. He stopped a moment and swallowed twice. Bart met his eyes.

"You can't stop now!" Bart mouthed at him, with his thin face as stern as the surgeon's might have been under the same circumstances. His blue eyes flashed a dare-do encouragement.

Gregory took his second needle, breathed deeply, continued. Though his inner tension heightened every time the old man moaned, though fears and doubts about his efficiency plagued him, the boy went on bravely. The whole business took about twenty minutes. Then Tullah and the farm lads carried the old farmer into the hospital room and made him comfortable.

"It wasn't too bad, was it?" Bart asked softly.

Gregory looked over at him heavily. "Awful," he mumbled. "I'll never be like Father. . . ."

"Don't you think he went through it too?" Bart asked. "What you're going through?" He began cleaning up swiftly.

"No!" Gregory snapped bluntly. He didn't want to talk; he wouldn't go into the kitchen when his mother called. He wouldn't let himself experience the sense of relief so many people seek after such a tense business. He was unconsciously cherishing his tightness and sensitivity. His father would have recognized his withdrawal and the reason for it, but Bart did not. He got Greg's chocolate and brought it into the surgery.

"Tullah must stay in the hospital room with the man," Gregory directed. "He might get restless or bleed. God forbid that he bleeds!"

"The young men have left; Tullah's gone to shut the gates," Bart reported. "I'll get him to bed down in the hospital when he comes in. You go on back to bed, Greg —'tis two o'clock and you must go to school tomorrow."

"He's right, son," Mistress Donlewis came to the top of the two steps leading down into the surgery from the passage.

Gregory stood twisting his fingers together, revealing his nervousness now. "Suppose . . . the man frets . . . and ails?"

If his mother felt for him, this was not the time to make a small boy of him. She smiled wisely and serenely. "If he does, we shall consider the problem then!"

Gregory finished his chocolate and told Bart to put out the surgery lanterns. He took a candle from the cabinet top himself and lighted his mother's way to the stair turn. Coming back to his own room, Greg snuffed the light quickly with little thought for Bart, who was still undressing. Throwing himself on the bed, Greg jolted Tawny and then ran his fingers in the dog's ruff. "Why must you hurt people to help them?" the surgeon's son wondered. The dog cocked a crooked ear at the prickle of his master's voice so close.

Bart murmured, "I don't know," sympathetically.

Greg kicked off his moccasins and rolled under the quilt with his clothes on; he wanted to brood, but the fatigue of the late hour and exhaustion from his labors overcame him and he slept even before Bart.

In the morning Gregory dressed the farmer's leg before he made ready for school. Everything seemed in order. The old man was awake and seemed brighter than the night before, but quite wan. He had undoubtedly lost a tremendous amount of blood.

Gregory was too absorbed during school to think often of the old man and his treatment. However, at dismissal, Greg rode home apace. All was well when he arrived. Bart reported that the farmer had eaten and drunk a little and was sleeping. The poor fellow sighed and moaned a good deal in his sleep and his limbs twitched, but he seemed to have little other distress.

Saturday went by equally well. Keith came back from the trip to Williamsburg at noon and was waiting with Bart at the drive gates when Greg arrived from the academy.

"I'm to go back for staying on the ninth," Keith announced, "when my classes will begin. Your patient's good, and Father should arrive any moment."

Greg dismounted and rubbed Patches's nose. "I wonder what Father will say?"

"What's to say?" Keith replied. "You surely did well enough what you had to do, from what Bart says."

Gregory's throat closed on such nonchalance. He could neither feel sure that he had done well nor yet that his father would approve of how he had done it.

When Stephen Donlewis did get home, a while later, he shed his dusty outer clothes immediately, for the best coach was not proof against the thick red dust of the turnpikes. Then he went directly into the hospital and narrowly regarded his son's handiwork. He prodded at the man's leg between ankle and knee and pushed gently at the suture edges. After the manner of doctors in general, he said nothing significant. Later, in the surgery, Gregory hung anxiously upon his comments, not daring to provoke them. Stephen Donlewis set himself a basin of hot water on the operating table and stripped to the waist and washed and got into a clean flannel shirt.

"So you had your emergency, eh?" the surgeon leaned on his left arm across the big table. "I needn't tell you, I suppose, that the first stitch is too deep and the fourth too shallow? Well, precision comes with experience!"

"Otherwise, sir?" Gregory asked, hesitant.

His father just nodded. "I ought to wash my hair; 'tis full of red sand!" he remarked, and then, "Beastly tourniquet they had on that leg, I take it; the ring still shows."

" 'Twas whipcord and I cut it off fast," Gregory said.

"Good boy! Get on to supper now; your mother's undoubtedly waiting."

Little more was said in regard to the case. The farmer's sons came to visit him that night. While the surgeon talked with them, Greg went about his business in the surgery proper and Bart studied prescriptions, perched on a high stool in the pharmacy room.

Sunday passed and on Monday morning, ready for school, Gregory was strapping his books into his saddlebag when Tullah hailed him and told him his father wanted him a moment in the hospital. The colored man took the pony's bridle.

Greg leaped over the gooseberry bushes near the waiting-room door. His father was fixing an abnormal twist on one of the restraining straps of the operating table with a pliers when Gregory dashed in.

"Ah, yes, I've something to show you," he said to his son and led the way toward the hospital door.

Greg knew of no new patients. Almost immediately he saw through the open doorway that there were none. Stopping just within, the doctor caught at his son's arm and held him back a moment. Greg washed cold all over with sudden anticipation. His father whispered to him. "Stay quiet; I will do any necessary talking!"

Then, shoving the boy gently before him, the surgeon pulled the covers from the farmer. The bandaging on the cut leg was blood-soaked, the pad beneath saturated. The old man knew something was to pay; he had felt the soggy wrapping and called the surgeon.

" 'Tis an evil development, I reckon?" the old fellow asked.

"It is that," the surgeon agreed.

"I feared from the beginning that I would lose the leg," the man murmured, "and the boy there, the mere boy, what did he know of't?"

Gregory's stomach fell apart inside; he hugged at his waistline, shocked. His father had not been checking the operating table for nothing—he was going to operate—to amputate the farmer's leg! Greg whitened as his father revealed what had happened: the ligation had eroded; even the sutures were rotting apart. The farmer's words bored into the boy: "the mere boy, what did he know of't?" But his father put firm fingers on his shoulders.

"He knew all he needed to know!" the doctor stated firmly. "These things happen; I was suspicious two days ago when I came home. I want the boy to learn to observe sharply. Look here, Gregory! You see the dark at the ankle and also up here around the edges where the too-tight stricture lay?" the surgeon pointed. "You can see the necrosis, the imminence of gangrene."

Gregory stood swallowing saliva in great gulps as he had the day at Merryhaven, as he always did when the sickness of his fear was upon him. His father's firm hand did not comfort him as the surgeon intended, for he shivered beneath it. Stephen Donlewis went on to tell the farmer what he had to do. The old man took the ultimatum of the operation with composure; he merely moaned that his old age would be pitiful and difficult.

"Go along now. I have Bart and Tullah; send Tullah in," the doctor said.

Gregory gave him a miserable, questioning look but the surgeon was already busy with the hemorrhaging blood vessel. Gregory ran out of the hospital room. He looked pitifully white and trembled when he took his reins from Tullah and whispered, "Father wants you in the surgery!" He had never been so glad of the long ride to school. All day long the farmer's question haunted him, pounding into a severe headache on his way home: "What did he know of't? The mere boy, what did he know of't?" Surely his father's words that such things happened and that he knew all he needed, surely these were just reassurances and it was his fault that the man had lost the leg! Troubled with this thinking as he pulled Patches to a walk in their drive, Gregory pretended not to see Bart waving to him from the dugout where he was piling waxed turnips.

But Bart came into the stable. "Did you have a good day?" he asked.

"You know!" Gregory blazed as his feeling spilled over. "I had a fine day, causing the old man's amputation! I did, you know I did! I must have done something wrong——"

Bart shook his head. "No, you didn't; your father told me. 'Twas the long time they took bringing him with that bad tourniquet on and——"

"I—I'm not going to make it, Bart—I'm quitting; I'm going to tell my father that I'll never be a surgeon like him," Gregory cried. He dropped Patches's saddle and ran headlong out of the stable. "You go be surgeon's apprentice if you think it's so easy!" he shouted over his shoulder. He ran around the stable and headed for his knoll. He curled his legs under him and sat pouting.

"Want your books? I unhooked your bag and put up your saddle—I figure you'll want to study if you're quittin' in the surgery," Bart's voice came sharply with just an edge of reprimand.

Gregory turned and looked up with his mouth pinched. Bart's expression was blank but hard. Both boys attempted to stare each other down. Then Bart said, "I'd kinda like to see you tell your old man you're through!"

Greg put his palms over his eyes. Bart sniffed.

"Gregory! You've got doctorin' in your blood; your trouble is that you think you're the only one in the world that learns anything the hard way! Your father understands you, Greg, and he expects you to make mistakes too. Don't you think he ever has? But you didn't on the old man, honest! Your father told me you might have used catgut instead of silk for both the ligation and the sutures but it wouldn't have made any difference——"

Gregory broke into hysterical tears. Bart stood by. When the surgeon's son had calmed down and wiped his eyes with the tail of his jacket, Bart asked, "Feel better?"

"I suppose . . ." Greg admitted.

"Now I'll tell you that your father wanted me to get you to get the whole business out of you—he's a very wise man, your father," Bart said admiringly.

Gregory nodded. "Is—is the old farmer all right—after the operation?" he asked and he noticed that his voice was quite steady.

"Uh-huh, restin' easy. You needn't go into the surgery unless the doctor calls you," Bart said. "Want to get your schoolwork done so we can look at the comet tonight if 'tis clear?"

That night, before Bart had come into their bedchamber, while Greg was packing his books for the next morning, Dr. Donlewis entered. He sat down beside his son on the bed. "You know now that you did no more wrong than any surgeon might have?" he asked directly.

"Yes, but sir, I—I shall be afraid to do anything like that again," Gregory stated honestly.

"Not when the time comes," his father assured him. "Surgery is a matter of the moment at hand; a situation arises and you go to meet it. I've told you many times that you start at a given moment and consider an immediate problem and look forward, never backward; and then pray to Almighty God that you divine well!" The doctor smiled his rare smile. " 'Tis a hard life, surgery, and often not very rewarding, though there are magnificent moments. Those keep a surgeon from dying a little with every death and breaking apart under each patient's pain; if you yearn not for the better way, the surer touch, the closer edge of truth, be not a surgeon, my son—but I need not tell you this!" He clapped the boy on the shoulder and got up and went out.

Gregory sat cherishing the quiet that settled around him, wondering whether he *was* worthy of his father's expectations.

XIX.

A Bout with the Apothecary

THE next evening the doctor was called to Merryhaven plantation just at suppertime. He returned about nine o'clock looking so glum that Gregory cautiously asked if he had lost a patient.

"Certainly not!" Dr. Donlewis replied, but explained no further.

Launa ladled out the doctor's supper from the big black iron pot she had kept on the crane over the coals. The surgeon rubbed his hands together before the hearth. Yet it was not particularly cold outside that night. A brisk, warmish wind rather indicated rain in the offing; shutters rattled everywhere. When Bart came in through the kitchen door with a cloth full of potatoes from the dugout, the breeze caught the door out of his hand. As he reached to grab it back, the potatoes burst from the corner of the cloth and rolled in every direction. Greg, doing homework at the end of the big kitchen table, giggled; even Launa laughed. Yet the doctor shouted at the poor boy.

"You oaf! Must you be so clumsy; see here, two potatoes in the fire!"

Flushing scarlet to the roots of his hair, Bart dived into the coals and rescued the potatoes and then stood sucking a scorched thumb.

"Part idiot, too, aren't you?" the surgeon asked, quite nastily.

Bart bit in his bottom lip and muttered, "Sorry, suh." He latched the door, put the potatoes away in Launa's box under the basin stand, and beat a hasty retreat from the doctor's view.

Margaret Donlewis, who had come in from the sewing room, asked her husband, "Did you see Philip about the medical supplies?"

The doctor nodded and finished his supper with a chunk of homemade bread, well buttered. "Just as I thought, the shipment has not come in, and won't! Confound this non-intercourse business. You know what this means, Meg, I shall have to send to Stewart now for opium and saffron and mercury, for I've hardly any. And me with yet a hundred and fifty dollars unpaid balance, heaven pity us!"

"Surely John Stewart trusts you, Steve?"

"Yes of course, but I like not to be beholden," the surgeon snapped.

Greg, looking up from his geometry, remembered Bart saying the same thing. Perhaps Greg's mother remembered too. "Steve, weren't you taking your worry out on the boy a moment agone?" she asked gently.

The doctor stopped chewing on his bread a second thoughtfully. "On Bart over the potatoes?" he asked then and finally nodded a bit sheepishly.

"He's a sensitive lad," Margaret murmured. "Let's not drive him to running off from us!"

The doctor nodded in agreement. Then he turned to Gregory and explained how the trade on the high seas was so upset that even the rich plantation owners like his brother Philip were losing money and ships and goods. The scarce foreign items that Stephen Donlewis usually purchased at bargain prices from his brother were not available. Greg would have to go immediately on the morrow to Mr. Stewart in Richmond and order an adequate supply for the winter months.

"I think you should take Bart along again," the doctor continued. "In fact, it being Saturday tomorrow, I can send him to meet you at noon dismissal and you will be part way."

Gregory gathered up his books and his slate.

"You tell Bart that I shall expect him to be pleasant and represent both him and me properly, tell him tonight!" the surgeon ordered.

Gregory did this dutifully. Bart whitened a little and reminded his friend that they had left the pharmacist on their other excursion more sour than they had reported to Dr. Donlewis.

"That's true; he didn't want to see you again, ever," Gregory said. "You'll have to come along though, because

Father doesn't know that and will likely write Mr. Stewart another note about you."

Bart nodded. "I suppose. It was about having to buy those expensive drugs that your father was so ill disposed toward me tonight, don't you think?" the boy continued.

"Yes, but I'm sure he didn't mean anything by't!" Greg responded quickly; he took note, too, of Bart's more sophisticated speech. The boy's diligence at reading was paying off.

"I—I don't suppose I can make John Stewart try me out, can I? Is there any way?" Bart asked next.

Gregory considered this, twisting a little finger through the cord that held his curls in a queue at his neck until he pulled it off. "You were going to give your butterfly wing to Mr. Stewart, remember?"

Bart agreed.

"I know you don't want to give it up, but if 'tis really a good piece—valuable, that is—you could borrow against it at a jeweler's. If Mr. Stewart saw that you did that, he might relent; in fact, he might suppose you to be quite clever and self-reliant, don't you think?" Greg suggested.

Bart considered this proposition and finally decided it was worth a try. He took his pin from its hiding place in his best-shirt pocket; both boys studied it lovingly and made their plans. They'd gallop wherever the road ran level to gain enough time to visit a jeweler's and get his evaluation of the pin.

The two boys worked their plan quite neatly. Gregory inquired as soon as they crossed the river and got the name of a reputable jeweler and watchmaker on Ninth near Broad, within view of the new capitol building.

Bart approached the jeweler with admirable self-assurance. "I'm to borrow as much as you can let me have against this," he stated boldly and not without some truth, "for my master, and he'd like to buy it back within three months, or else, if need be, you may sell it!"

The jeweler looked the pin over carefully on both sides and then examined it more thoroughly with a glass magnifier.

"Who is your master, boy?" he asked.

"The surgeon Donlewis of Fairville."

"Hm, does he realize that this would be much more valuable if he had the other half? It's been broken—see here."

Bart carried it off as if he had known all along, and perhaps he had. "Yes, sir, 'tis an old piece and the other part has been lost."

"What a pity," the man murmured. "Well," he said at last, "I could let you have about thirty dollars." The boys had to keep watch that they did not gasp in glee at what seemed to them a very tidy sum. The jeweler continued, "If your master wishes to sell later, rather than redeem, I will give him a proper price. The jewels are genuine and of a fair size."

Bart took a deep breath and asked, "About—how much, d'ye think?"

"We must check the prices of such gems in Baltimore and New York, but better than a hundred dollars—quite a bit better, perhaps." The jeweler eyed the two boys then with an inkling of suspicion. "You're not, by chance, your own and not the surgeon's agent? And wi' his goods?" He asked suddenly.

"He's telling true," Greg thrust in. "He is my father's bonded boy and I am Gregory Donlewis, the surgeon's son. We're going to pay the money you give to an apothecary here in Richmond, would you wish to check. My father did not receive an expected shipment of drugs which were prepaid—the hard times, you know." He could run words out smoothly, too, once he was started.

To their surprise the jeweler counted out thirty-five dollars from a metal coffer, most of it in good Dutch and English coin. Bart took a last, loving look at his pin and then accepted the money, which he put carefully into the doctor's purse that had held nothing more this time than a note begging the apothecary's consideration. As the boys closed the door upon the cosy little jewelry shop, Bart asked Gregory whether he thought his mother would understand what he had done.

"Yes, she would," Greg replied thickly. Then he added that he hoped they could carry things off half as well with old Stewart as they had with the watchmaker. They decided that they must try his mood and temper before they even mentioned the money.

Accordingly Gregory gave the old gentleman his father's list immediately. Stewart shuffled into his back room to pack the items in crocks, which he sealed with cloth strips and wax. He hadn't even seemed to notice Bart behind Greg. Both boys waited taut with anxiety for his return. Finally he came toward the counter where Greg had laid his saddlebag.

"You put these in carefully, y'hear; they should be cushioned against breaking," the old man cautioned.

Bart stepped forward to open the saddlebag straps. He knew he had to get it over sometime, the meeting with the Scotsman. "I know that, sir," he murmured.

Stewart fixed steely blue eyes upon him. "You again, eh? Haunting me? Now isn't your master a stubborn, diehard fellow? He will please to remember that he is your master and he'll stay so, ye understand?"

Bart felt his cheeks reddening; he lost his self-confidence swiftly. "He—he had me to come along wi' Greg," he whispered.

"Aye, for he figures to wear down my resistance, but

I don't see as you've anything about you to wear it down wi'."

Bart stood quietly as though in complete agreement with this opinion, and Gregory wanted to poke him. Instead of hanging his head as he tucked away the medicines, Bart should have smiled brightly and joked off the remark.

"What did you tell me your father did?" Mr. Stewart asked quite suddenly and unexpectedly, so that Bart tossed up his head, surprised.

"I don't believe I said, suh, but he was a traveling actor," Bart answered.

"An actor? Have mercy!" the apothecary shrieked. "You tell Stephen Donlewis that I'd as soon have the devil himself as the son of an actor in my shop!"

Bart felt his hurt rising behind his eyes and would not give in to it. He bristled instead and rose to the occasion. "My father died when I was very small, but my mother told me he was a good and worthy man!"

"Indeed? And this mother, who was she?" Stewart asked.

"Jessica Worrell," Bart replied.

"And before she was Worrell, who was she? Know ye not?" the apothecary prodded.

"No, suh," Bart, choking up, whispered.

"Ashamed to tell ye, eh? Respectable girl who ran off wi' a two-bit actor maybe, or maybe not," Stewart snapped.

Bart tossed back his head and spoke plainly then. "My mother was an actress—in the real theayter; she acted in New York and Phillydelphy and—and even here in Richmond, I—think . . ." he gulped hard and went on rather fast, as though he were chasing the words across the counter toward the old man. "She weren't ashamed of being an actress because she loved the real theayter——"

"Hush!" John Stewart commanded. "I'm agin' the theater, ye hear, and therefore I'll never take you off Stephen Donlewis's hands. Now out, boy, and don't darken my door again. The doctor's son here is big enough," he fixed a sharp eye and a pointed finger on Gregory, "to tote his father's business. Ye are not to come here again, Worrell, ye hear?"

"Yes, suh," Bart murmured, completely intimidated.

Gregory thought right then that Bart would walk out without remembering the money from the pin. But when he had almost reached the door, Bart gathered himself together, turned, and faced the pharmacist again. Opening the doctor's purse, he strode back to the counter and shook out a shower of coins before the astonished Stewart.

"There!" Bart cried hoarsely. " 'Tis my own money and though 'tis not much, you will please to write the amount of it from Dr. Donlewis's account and gi' me a receipt—and I'll bring you more later on if I get any, or send it if ye'll not admit me!"

Gregory wanted to cry "Bravo!" but the apothecary glared upon the money and then counted it with a pointed index finger and demanded, "Nigh onto forty dollars in our money value; where should the likes of you get that? The doctor be not paying you a wage?"

"No, suh. I sold my pin," Bart blurted. "You wouldn't take it against the debt so I sold it."

John Stewart stared across his counter; the veins in his forehead pulsed and his scalp pinked under his handsome white hair; his mouth worked wordlessly for a moment. Finally he grumbled aloud, "Sold your pin? For this amount? Idiot, fool, knew you not its value? Take your money, you dolt!"

"No, suh," Bart held his ground. "I've given it you

170

against the doctor's medicine account and I want a receipt."

"You do, eh? You'll wait on it!" Stewart sneered.

Bart knotted his fingers into fists, uncertain what he could do. Even Greg stood nonplused. Who were they to coerce a man like John Stewart?

The apothecary grumbled incoherently, something about "forty dollars—a dozen precious stones—idiot—" Suddenly he said firmly, "I'm not dishonest. I'll send a receipt to your master. Now get out!"

Gregory came to Bart's rescue, for the lad stood dejected, head down, his fingernails working his palms raw. "He didn't sell the pin, Mr. Stewart. The jeweler was honest; he said if Bart really wants to sell the pin later, he will give him a proper price, enough money to pay off all of Father's debt. G–good day, sir!" Opening the door, Gregory shoved Bart through it. "Come on, we've done enough damage for one time, I'd say," he observed.

Clattering across the bumpy cobblestones on their ponies, the boys could not talk, nor yet on the rattly wooden planks of the two-part covered bridge, but once on the Petersburg pike it was easier riding. Bart worried that he had neither pin nor receipt. Gregory assured him that the old pharmacist, though crusty, was just. He would reduce the Donlewis account, perhaps by more than thirty-five dollars. Gregory thought the pin must have considerable value, since both jeweler and apothecary had been impressed with it.

"It certainly made a better impression than I did," poor Bart remarked grimly. "I'm really in a fix. Whatever shall I tell your father? Mr. Stewart didn't give me any kind of statement for the new drugs either, in all the excitement."

"That's true, he didn't; well, we shall just tell Father

that he probably forgot and will post one or send it along on the Petersburg coach," Greg suggested.

"I—I don't think it'll be easy to tell your father that, for he'll want to know all about everything."

"Yes, I'll bet he will," Greg admitted.

XX.

No Confidence

THE two boys worried the whole way home and arrived at no satisfactory explanation to offer the doctor. But the moment they entered the Donlewis kitchen they discovered that temporarily, at least, they had nothing to fear. Dr. Donlewis had been called to Norfolk to attend an old senator. An elaborate note on the operating table ordered Gregory's life for the next several days. His father expected to return Wednesday night. He wrote:

Deliver the two prescriptions to Jackson's tonight

Change dressing on Jake Benjamin's knee tomorrow

Do anything required within limits I set the last time
I went away

Keep the surgery and pharmacy in good order

Have Bart make sassafras cough syrup and send
bottle to Dawes family

Take both Bart and Tullah with you if you must go
to any emergency from here; try to avoid going
out but don't hesitate if someone's life is in danger; clumsy help is better than no help at all

Bart and Keith may clear the north field with Mal-

colm but you are to remain in surgery or pharmacy
whenever you are not at school

Do your duty as you did it last time; I was not displeased.

Greg smiled at that, it was so like his father; he'd not
come right out and say he was pleased but merely that he
was not displeased. Gregory grumbled about staying in
the surgery though. Malcolm was clearing their last virgin
land for winter wheat; all the boys had enjoyed helping
him late afternoons as he sawed away ambitiously, bare-
chested in the warmish fall weather. Keith, fretting im-
patiently upon his departure date, was particularly glad
of the outdoor work. Malcolm certainly welcomed extra
hands. Even Bart left Greg to sit glumly at the doctor's
desk and went to help load cut logs into the wagon to
drive to Malcolm's cabin, on which he was adding two
rooms to be ready for his marriage to a young lady from
Richmond at Christmas.

All went well through Sunday. Several people came for
minor doctoring. Greg dispensed paregoric for diarrhea
and calomel for fever. Monday, the fourth of November,
was a flamingly beautiful day. Gregory arrived from
school to find everyone except his mother in the north field
as Malcolm finished up the last woodsy stretch.

"Don't see why I can't go too," Greg protested as he
drank the cider his mother had set out for him with two
molasses cookies. "Anyone could reach me at the field in
two minutes."

"Anyone?" Margaret Donlewis chuckled. "I, for example, I could pick up my skirts and run out there for
you?"

After they laughed heartily together Greg pouted
again, proving he was still very much a boy. "I wasn't
here all day!" he protested.

"True, but you *are* here now; suppose your father came home unexpectedly and found you derelict in your duties and not following his instructions?" his mother asked.

"None of us would like it!" he admitted, grinning. Still nibbling the last cooky, he went into the surgery and then eyed the pharmacy. Everything was as neat and shining clean as an altar on Easter. Bart had evidently done all the work he could find before taking off to help Malcolm. Feeling more reconciled to his fate, Gregory got out a pharmaceutical recipe book and began reading in it idly.

He was presently interrupted by shouting and the rumble of fast-rolling wheels. Then someone pulled a field wagon up beside the waiting-room door with such clatter that Greg left his book precipitately and ran outside.

"Greg! Greg! Are you there? Has Father got back, by any chance?" It was Malcolm shouting.

Gregory saw that someone lay flat in the wagon bed and seemed literally covered with blood. Malcolm had Arne with him; Bart jumped from the wagon back and ran around to hold the horses steady. Gregory knew that it must be Keith who was hurt. Malcolm lifted the still form carefully and carried it into the surgery to the couch, Arne helping.

"Father?" Malcolm asked again.

"He's still gone," Gregory muttered. He looked stunned, faced with what he knew must be a serious doctoring problem.

Arne went out to take charge of the wagon and Bart came running in. "Greg, do something!" he cried.

Greg set his teeth resolutely and threw his shoulders back with his determination. He went to look closely at Keith. "What happened?" he asked.

"I don't know exactly. He was alone with the wagon and must have fallen from the seat; he managed to drive back somehow to where I was; then he fainted. You had better do what you can right away. I tied a rag around to stop the bleeding; it was bleeding badly," Malcolm told.

"You shouldn't have done it like that," Greg stated, steadying under the realization that his knowledge of the matter was certainly superior to Malcolm's. Quickly he removed the rag Malcolm had fixed too tightly. The jagged cut on Keith's upper arm, from which a piece of bone protruded, seeped blood immediately but not as violently as Greg had been led to expect. Bart, at Gregory's direction, took over putting pressure upon a clean compress laid over the wound. Greg ran an unstoppered bottle of spirits of camphor beneath Keith's nose. The lad came to and moaned. His mother had heard of the accident from Arne and she fixed some brandy in water and got it into Keith as soon as he could swallow. Greg cut off his brother's torn and bloody shirt and cleaned him up. Then he bound a long splint and straightened the arm out against it somewhat.

By this time it was getting dark and supper was almost ready in the kitchen. Revived by the brandy, Keith told what had happened to him. He'd been moving a log in the wagon bed preparatory to tumbling it out and his foot had slipped. He jarred against the log end, which was precariously balanced on the wagon side; it spun back and struck him sidewise and knocked him out of the wagon headfirst. His left arm hit the already stacked log ends of the pile he was making and snapped above the elbow. It also scraped along the roughhewn edges as he slipped groundward in the fall.

As Keith talked, Gregory noticed that the arm began to bleed profusely again; he put his fingers in the brachial control point in Keith's neck and held and released almost automatically. The doctor's clock bonged seven-thirty.

175

Margaret Donlewis suggested that Malcolm check on the wagon and his unfinished work and come back for supper. She sent a tray in for Greg and Keith. The younger boy ate ravenously but Keith was in considerable pain and also worried; he would touch nothing. Gregory got some laudanum and gave him two teaspoonfuls. It made him sleepy but he couldn't relax enough to fall off.

Just at deep dark a horse sounded at their drive gate and Bart came running from the kitchen.

"There, good! That must be Father arriving!" Greg cried in relief to Keith. "Your arm should be set and sutured; the cut's very deep."

Keith moaned softly. A moment later Greg grumbled in disappointment. Bart had admitted a patient who wanted to renew a soothing ointment the doctor had prescribed for the boils with which he was plagued. Bart took care of the matter. Gregory went back to Keith.

"I don't much like leaving you undoctored," he said. "Father may come tonight or tomorrow or again he may not; he wasn't sure, you know."

Keith looked up, frowning. "You let be," he said emphatically.

Gregory gulped in the hurt feeling that overwhelmed him and took the supper tray back to the kitchen. There he told his mother what he had told Keith, that he did not think the arm should be left untreated.

"Why? Is't dangerous?" his mother asked.

"It could be," Greg returned cautiously: in his heart he thought it was dangerous, especially an upper-limb compound fracture. His father had always emphasized the fact that gangrene could start readily in an upper limb. "I'd better pull the arm straighter, anyhow, later on."

"You don't think you should wait, still, for your father?"

He gave his mother a stark, questioning look. "Don't you think I can do it?"

"It isn't that," Margaret said quickly. "I should think it would just be better . . . if your father were here."

Greg walked around one of the kitchen chairs slowly, fingering its back with his index finger. "Yes, it would certainly be better," his voice almost trembled with bitterness. He went back to the surgery.

At ten o'clock, with no sign of the surgeon, Bart came in from the pharmacy where he'd been reading and beckoned Greg to the railing. He was of the same opinion as Gregory, that something should be done for Keith. He prodded the surgeon's son in no uncertain terms.

"At least straighten the arm out and weight it down, as your father did my leg before he set it, remember?"

"All right." Gregory swung a lantern close to the couch. Keith opened heavy eyes under its glare. "I'm going to pull your arm straight," Greg told him firmly.

"I'd just as soon you left well enough alone," Keith snarled.

Gregory pulled up. "What do you mean?" he asked.

"Just that I'd rather not lose my arm," Keith returned.

Until that moment Gregory had not consciously thought at all of the old farmer whose leg had been amputated. Chill fear washed over him. His palms went clammy; the old sickness came up hot in him, a thick slime of bile in his mouth; he went onion-white. However, he fought valiantly against the paralyzing tension that mounted in him; he chewed fiercely at his underlip. Nerving steady, he replied with a hard little mouth. "You'll be more like to lose it if I do nothing!" He poured out another dose of laudanum. "Here, drink this, it will help some against the pain."

Determined, then, Gregory called for Malcolm and Tullah to hold Keith quiet. He bound weights to Keith's wrist and then, with Bart's help, pulled the arm to almost normal length, getting the bone end back into the flesh. Keith screamed twice but afterward he was more comfortable and lay still. A blood clot swept from the bleeder and Greg was obliged to affix a padded tourniquet above the break and keep Bart watching and releasing it.

Poor Greg walked the surgery floor restlessly as the night progressed, hoping and praying upon his father's return, though he could hardly expect him now before morning. As the hours ticked away, Gregory became more convinced that he ought to set the bone and ligate the bleeder and suture. Shortly before one he went into the kitchen. His mother was still sitting up, sewing before the fireplace, but her mind was not much on the work. She looked up immediately.

"I—I don't think we should wait—with Keith . . ." Greg began.

"Is there actual danger in waiting for your father?" his mother asked again.

Greg told the truth, as he stood rolling his fists into balls. "Yes, I'm sure there is; Father has told me many times that a broken arm can infect or become gangrenous more readily and faster than a leg; Keith's arm is swelling badly and though clots form and stop the bleeding, they wash out and it starts all over. I have put on a tourniquet and Bart's watching it, but I don't like waiting! Yet I don't want to do it alone, either, especially because Keith doesn't want me to. He's afraid! He's afraid I'll do something wrong as—as with that farmer."

"Did you do anything wrong?" Margaret asked. "I thought you did not."

"Father said I did not do anything wrong," Gregory said firmly, but his face worked and he could taste his nausea again. "It—it doesn't always turn out right, doctoring."

His mother stood up and pulled him into her arms a moment. "I know, I know that, Greg, for I have seen your father broken with failure sometimes," she whispered. "Do what you think best for Keith, my son; you must do that because your father left you in charge."

"If Father doesn't come, then, in half an hour, I shall try to set the bone," Gregory decided. "If I succeed, I can close the wound and take care of everything necessary. Please ask Mal to come up; I'll need him."

The doctor did not come. But Keith raised a row and would not let Gregory touch him. He reared up quite nastily and neither Malcolm nor Bart could persuade him.

"Get me a doctor, you hear, a real surgeon! I want to go to college whole or not at all!" the lad bellowed.

"You're being unreasonable and unfair," Malcolm told him. "No other surgeon's available within a half day's ride and none anywhere so good with fractures as Father; Greg's watched and helped him time and again."

Gregory went about gathering what he would need with a set mouth. He had already spent considerable time fixing a proper splint and bandages toward his father's arrival, so those were ready. At length he brought Keith an opium tablet, but the young man threw it back in his face.

"Look, you're not going to touch me any more than you have! You've probably done enough damage—let be!" Keith cried.

Their mother looked between them and Malcolm shook his head. Margaret was not sure whether the gesture was intended for Keith or for Greg. On the far side of the operating table, where Gregory had set two bright lamps, Bart stood tensely twisting his fingers. The room was tight with tension. Finally Mistress Donlewis suggested in a troubled voice that they wait until morning.

"That is what I believe we should not do," Gregory stated.

"Wait!" his mother insisted.

Her youngest son looked squarely at her. "You, too," he bit out, then, "you're afraid of how I would do it! Well, let be!" he turned, flung open the wooden railing gate between surgery and waiting room and slid through. In a moment he had unlatched the outside door and was gone into the darkness.

XXI.

Greg Goes It Alone

"GREG!" Mistress Donlewis called out the waiting-room door despairingly. But the chilly dark was entirely quiet.

"I'll get him back," Bart volunteered. "Someone must watch that tourniquet!"

"Take your jacket and one of his," Malcolm suggested practically, for he knew how cold it had turned.

By the time Bart got out with the two jackets, he could find no trace of Greg anywhere. He walked around house, stable, barn, and looked just everywhere he could think, but to no avail. Chagrined, at long last he came back to the surgery. Malcolm was sitting with Keith. Bart wondered if they had talked at all of Greg's going off, but he did not ask.

No one got any rest that night. Mistress Donlewis could not go to bed and kept wandering about. Tullah went out searching an hour after Bart's return and again at daybreak, but he did not find Gregory.

" 'Tis a fine state of affairs," Malcolm observed severely when Launa brought ham, eggs, and chocolate into the surgery for breakfast.

Keith was in great pain and could not eat anything. "I'm sorry," he admitted finally. "I shouldn't have hurt his feelings. I reckon I could let him do what he would wi' me now. Is anyone looking for him?"

"Everyone's looked but me; 'tis my turn," Malcolm offered and turned Keith over to Tullah.

Bart stood by. At seven o'clock a galloping horse in the drive roused hope of the surgeon's return, but it proved to be an anxious husband.

"Where is the doctor?" the man demanded.

Bart told him.

"Ah, yes, you're the boy that helps with prescriptions. My wife, Asa—I'm George Pryor—my wife has a bad heart and is in one of her attacks. We've no more medicine left after what I gave her before I left home. Can you give me some quickly, quickly, boy? Time is important."

Bart felt excitement tearing at him. He was almost certain that the doctor gave Mistress Pryor a medicine compounded from digitalis, foxglove. He hurried into the apothecary room and found to his dismay that the large bottle in which the tincture of digitalis was kept was empty. Bart had never made that prescription alone. If only Greg were there—— He returned to the waiting room. "I—I have to get the doctor's son to mix some," he confessed. "It won't take long. Please sit down."

"Remember, time is important," Mr. Pryor repeated, but he did sit down.

Bart ran outside, not sure where he should go. He could see that nobody was over by the spring; Malcolm beyond the mulberry-tree lane waved a negative gesture, so he was coming back unsuccessful. Outside the side barn door Tawny stood sniffing and wagging his tail. Even before the dog's presence registered with Bart, the door opened in and Arne came out with the milk pails. Tawny bolted between his legs, nearly knocking the poor lad off balance. The dog ran *into* the barn. Bart with a sudden inspiration, tore after the dog. Tawny headed for a set of big cribs or feed bins built into the back wall. Bart had not thought of these during his search though all the boys knew about them. Malcolm could remember when the cribs had had sliding back panels which he said had been put there during the War for Independence to make hiding places for scouts and prisoners. But when Dr. Donlewis had to put a new rear wall on the barn the back panels had gone. The front panels bolted up from the floor and Bart was sure Gregory was hiding behind one. He shouted loudly. "Greg! *Greg!* D'ye hear? Listen to me, you must come right away. Mistress Pryor's like to die, you hear? Greg Donlewis, what kind of surgeon you goin' to be?"

The dog was snuffling at the middle crib panel. Bart tried to pull it down, but it was fixed tight and he knew there must be a hook on the interior side as well as the bolt on the exterior. The dog whined, then looked at Bart and wagged his tail. Bart thumped on the panel with his fist and the dog leaped up and licked his hand. A soft bumping stirred behind the crib panel then. Bart renewed his verbal efforts. "Greg! Open up! I know you're in there. You've got to do what you can because no one else can do anything!"

Gregory was in the crib, where he'd been nursing his hurt feelings angrily after a first spell of violent crying. Bart luckily chose words which brought back Dr. Donlewis's note of directions sharply: "Don't hesitate if someone's life is in danger; clumsy help is better than no help." Gregory unbolted the inner latch. His face was swollen and dirty and he was cramped from sitting.

Bart did not scold. "Hurry," he said matter-of-factly.

"Can you make that foxglove stuff for Mistress Pryor? She took her last drop a while ago and our bottle's empty. Does it take long to make it?"

Greg shook his head. "The elixir's all made and the other ingredients ready—gi' me your kerchief. I'm a mess, aren't I?"

Bart nodded. "Go in kitchen and douse your head at the pump. What should I set out?"

"The green elixir and powdered digitalis and some sugar," Greg said. "How's Keith?"

"Ready to have you help him now," Bart returned.

"No!" Greg said hotly. "I'll make the stuff for Mistress Pryor, that's different, but Keith must wait for Father. I can't touch him, Bart; I was sick in there, actually sick, thinking . . . 'tis well I did nothing more."

Bart swung around before him and for a second Gregory thought he was going to hit him. "You listen, Gregory Donlewis," Bart snapped, "your father outlined your duty and you have to do it! That arm's waited too long already—remember what you told me when I was in that shack and how I nearly died, waitin'. Keith's arm is worse'n my leg was!" This was perfectly sound and Gregory, knowing it, flushed and made no further protest.

The boys parted company. Bart went to encourage Mr. Pryor and begin the prescription. Gregory cleaned up in the kitchen. Soon Mr. Pryor galloped off, content, and Greg steeled himself to go into the surgery. Bart put firm hands on his shoulders.

"Don't go in unless you will do what you must!" he advised. "Don't think about hurting Keith, don't listen to what he says or what anyone else says. Think about saving his life, that's the important thing, you've *got* to, Greg. Now go on—shall I bring the brandy?"

In spite of himself, Gregory had to admire Bart's goading.

Bart got some laudanum into Keith, who tried to be quiet yet fought the effects of the drug. He was wide awake when Gregory cleaned the now puffy wound with brandy as his father had done with Bart's leg. Keith struggled against his pain but perhaps not as much as he could have. The first time he screamed, Gregory got horribly sick and ran into the pharmacy to relieve himself and get firm hold on his nerves. He came back with the determination to conquer his nausea and fear. As Bart had suggested, he shut his ears against Keith's cries and also against the nasty things the suffering youth shouted, some of them in language his father would scarcely have approved. The whole procedure was nerve-racking not merely for Greg but for Bart and Malcolm as well. The exertion of the setting caused perspiration to pour out onto the neck of Greg's shirt; he worked on doggedly, gulping down his wretched sickness. He tied off the artery successfully and, with Malcolm pulling Keith's lower arm to give him enough traction, he got the ends of the broken humerus together properly. At that point Keith fainted; Greg did the suturing of the tear and the bandaging and the first winding of the splint before he brought his brother around again. Bart finished the bandaging.

Mistress Donlewis made a basin of eggnog and everyone had a cup after Gregory finished with the arm. Keith found himself considerably relieved of pain now and was able to sit up part way and drink some refreshment too. Afterward, with Malcolm accompanying him, Keith proved quite capable of walking upstairs to his own bed. Mal decided to stay on with him.

Gregory sipped his cup of eggnog when he was finally alone in the quiet surgery; a moment later he ran into the pharmacy and tossed it all up. The doctoring over, he was sick a long time; he shut the door even on Bart and fought with himself again. Suppose Keith did eventually lose his arm, as the poor farmer had his leg? It was an awful possibility, yet Greg had seen no immediate signs of trouble. His mother, wise woman that she was, let him alone.

Later Gregory began patiently to clean up the things he had somewhat disordered. A little past noon his mother sent in his lunch. When she came to find out if he had eaten it, she suggested that he go to bed, since he'd had no sleep the night before.

"Keith's asleep," she reported, "and your father will likely not get home now until late tonight or early tomorrow."

Greg nodded and nibbled at the food.

XXII.

All the Pieces Fit Together

GREGORY was willing to go to bed. However, in his room he sat awhile without turning down the coverlet, rubbing his fingers in Tawny's thick wool. He was still fully dressed when a loud knock sounded upon the front house door. Bart ran down the passage from the kitchen to answer the knock. It was probably not a patient, since patients seldom came to the main house door. Greg peeked into the hall, however, to see.

"Bundle from the post coach from Richmond," a fellow called, handing the packet of letters to Bart.

"Look and see if there's a letter from John Stewart to Father," Greg whispered as Bart came by. "That will be the bill, you know."

"None says," Bart answered. "Here, you look; per-

haps you'd know his hand. They're all for your father."
He turned over the packet.

"They're not all for Father," Greg cried in a moment.
"One's for you—see here: To *Master Jebart Worrell* at
the house of the Surgeon Donlewis. Come on in. . . ."

Bart closed the bedroom door behind him. Greg set
the pile of letters on a dresser and handed Bart his. The
boy stood staring at it a moment; he had never received
a letter in his life and had no reason to expect one.

"Break the seal," Greg urged. "Do you want me to go
out?"

"No, no—you open it," Bart suggested, but Greg
wouldn't. With his fingers all thumbs Bart got the seal
to crack and unfolded the large square cover paper. Inside was a finely written note and another fold of sealed
paper. Bart read the note aloud slowly. It was from the
jeweler with whom he had left his butterfly wing.

Master Worrell, I beg to inform you that the
apothecary, John Stewart, be interested in purchasing
the article you so kindly left on appraisal with me
the third this instant and proposes that you accept
the enclosed statement in full payment. Please ad-
vise your disposition toward this proposal at your
earliest convenience.

"Whatever does it mean?" Bart wondered.

"You'll not know until you open the other paper,"
Gregory assured him, piqued by the mystery.

Bart broke the other seal and found that the note read:

To date, fourth November 1811, all indebtedness
paid in full in re: account of Stephen Donlewis, Surgeon, Esquire, signed:

The signature, Bart knew, would await his decision. His

lips moved over the statement again and again, especially the "all indebtedness paid in full." He looked anxiously at Gregory. " 'Twas my mother's," he whispered, "all I had of her."

Gregory swallowed hard too. How could he help his friend with a decision like that? He said the only thing he knew to be certain. "No matter what, Bart, Mr. Stewart is honest. He must want the pin and he would not cheat you."

Bart sat down stiffly on his side of the bed with the papers in his hand. For a long time he barely moved. Gregory stretched out on the coverlet and rolled his head into the crook of his elbow. He nearly fell asleep. Bart startled him when he jumped up, saying, "I shall do it, I shall let him have it, for I owe it to you and your father!"

"No, no! Bart, don't do anything hasty. We can talk to Father and go to see Mr. Stewart," Greg suggested.

Little did the boys know that such planning was unnecessary. For not more than half an hour later Launa came looking for Bart and Greg both. "Man in kitchen," was all she said.

And it was old John Stewart, wrapped up in a shawl and warming his hands at the fire. He had driven into their driveway and come unannounced to the kitchenway.

"Bart, did you receive a letter in that packet on the post coach?" Mistress Donlewis asked the boy as soon as he appeared.

"Yes'm," he admitted and felt in his pocket for the papers.

Old Stewart turned his steely eyes upon him. "Ye ken, young Worrell, about the pin, eh? And am I to have it?"

Bart took a long breath. "Yes, suh, I've decided, if you will please to sign the receipt so I may give it the doctor," he said in a quite steady voice.

But Gregory saw him blink fast and he interrupted. "He doesn't want to give it up, Mr. Stewart, 'tis all he has of his mother's——"

"You keep out o' this," the apothecary snapped at him, and Mistress Donlewis raised an anxious finger of warning.

Bart unfolded the indebtedness statement upon the end of the table and took the inkpot and quill from their shelf beside the hearth. Very deliberately, and with certain large flourishes, the old Scotsman wrote "J. Stewart" upon the signature line while Gregory watched Bart's struggle to contain his emotion at his loss. The boy got a sand sprinkler and sanded the writing. Stewart cleared his throat half a dozen times as though bringing himself toward an announcement; then he pulled a great silk kerchief from under his carriage cape and unfolded its many folds with as much ceremony as a performing magician. "Now, boy, you claim this was your mother's, eh?" he asked and held out in his left palm the jewel-studded butterfly wing.

"Yes, s–sir," Bart stuttered.

"Then see here," Mr. Stewart unclasped his other hand and therein lay the other wing! Identical it was, except that the letter was an *S* in seed pearls instead of *J;* the filigree work and the other jewels were the same.

Everyone gasped in surprise.

"And your mother was named Jessica and was in the theater, eh?" the old man continued.

Bart nodded and explained how he had come to be named Jebart for both his parents.

"An old man canna be angry and lonely forever, Jebart Stewart Worrell, ye hear. When my daughter wanted to run off with the theatrical company that was playing at Shockoe Hill Theater one summer, I told her she was no daughter o' mine and should not wear her mother's pin, which she had on. We've hot tempers, we Stewarts —'twas your bit o' temper that sent ye to pawn your pin to pay your bounden debt that drew me to ye, Jebart, 'twas indeed!" He shook a bony finger in the boy's face. "Well, she said, did Jessica, I remember the words: 'then take your Stewart and I'll change my name,' and she snapped off the half of't and threw it at me. I never saw her again, Jebart, boy, and I was grave hurt. I never knew what became of her and 'twas many years before I could stuff my pride behind me and try to discover whom and where she married. 'Twas too late then!"

"She be buried in Frederick, Maryland, sir, and I could take you," Bart whispered.

"May the guid Laird bless Dr. Donlewis for takin' your papers, boy, or ye'd been lost to me forever. Now, lad, I'll be havin' your pin fixed proper and my back room made into a little bedroom as it was when my dear wife died and left me your mother, Jessica. And next Sunday, wi' the doctor's kind permission, we'll light our pipes wi' your indenture papers and you'll come home for good, eh, boy?"

Large round tears were stealing down Bart's cheeks as he stood stunned by this remarkable turn of affairs. John Stewart, crusty old John Stewart, was his grandfather and he would get to study the arts and secrets of pharmacopoeia after all, as his very inheritance ought dictate! The crotchety Stewart said nothing more and required nothing of the astonished boy. He went off with his driver in his small closed carriage, but he left the two butterfly wings on the Donlewis kitchen table along with the signed receipt for Stephen Donlewis. It was Margaret Donlewis who said gently into the long silence after his departure, "Are you not proud to have found a family, Jebart?"

He looked at her gratefully and murmured a "Yes'm."

And it was Gregory who sat apart with Bart before supper as they talked out their experiences in excitement and delight yet with a touch of sadness, for the coming separation. Supper itself was almost gay with Keith at table and Greg relating the whole story of his plotting with Bart to pay the doctor's account off, the selfsame story the two boys had been so worried might come to light the Saturday before.

At bedtime neither boy could sleep, despite the strain of the previous night. It was very, very late, Greg supposed, when the sound of hoofbeats sparked again in their driveway, startling in the dead of the night. The pounding came closer and closer and then stopped near by. It must be the doctor at last. Gregory could not get moving to meet him after he had jumped out of bed. His legs seemed glued to the floor.

Stephen Donlewis came in through the kitchen, seeing the light his wife had been about to extinguish.

"Oh, Steve!" she went to him eagerly.

"It's raining," he mentioned as he slung off his big cape and tossed his hat upon the washstand. He took his wife in his arms tenderly. "Is something the matter that you're up so late?"

She plunged into the story of Keith's arm. "We waited and waited; finally Gregory set the bone. I—wasn't so sure he should, Steve, but we had no idea when you would come," Margaret finished anxiously.

"Greg should know what he's doing on a thing like that," her husband replied calmly.

"Keith was very upset; he remembered that farmer— and so did I, Steve, I could not help it——"

"Hush!" the doctor cried sharply.

But it was too late; Gregory had come to the kitchen doorway at last; he heard and understood what his mother said. He stood there silent with his face working.

"Come here, my son," the surgeon beckoned to him.

Greg ran across the space between them and buried his face in his father's soft, ruffled cravat. "Suppose he should lose his arm—Keith—suppose he should!" he cried and the whole misery of his experience tore loose from him in great dry sobs of anxiety. "Oh, please, my father, go upstairs and look at him. Take off the splint and see if I have done it right, *please!*"

"Hush, now, get hold of yourself," his father put his firm, comforting hands upon the boy's shoulders.

"No one, no one believes in me—Keith didn't, Mother doesn't!" Greg cried.

The doctor turned up his face by cupping his chin in his palm. "I do! I believe in you or I'd not have left you in the surgery," he stated clearly. "Now answer me what I ask. Has Keith had any severe pain since you set the broken bone?"

"No."

"Has he any fever?" Greg shook his head. "Has there been any swelling or streaking above or below the region of the break?" Again the answer was negative. "Did you notice anything at all unusual while you were working on the bone or the wound? Any of the signs of gangrene that I have taught you to recognize?"

"No, sir."

"Where is Keith?"

"Upstairs asleep in his bed," Gregory lifted his head now and looked timidly at his father, who had become as level-mouthed as usual.

"Now, suppose you were I and I had just reported to you all that you have just told me—think, boy! Would you rush upstairs and tear apart my work—would you?" the surgeon demanded.

Gregory hesitated. Then he admitted, "No, sir, I guess not."

"Well, then, just before Keith leaves for Williamsburg next week, I will look at the setting and perhaps put on a cast. Now is there anything else you need tell me?" Stephen Donlewis smiled just a little.

Relieved and also released from his terrible responsibility, Gregory plunged into recital of the astonishing news about Bart and the pharmacist while his mother made hot cider. She went upstairs before the doctor, who checked the surgery for the night with his son.

"Father," Greg said with his hand upon his bedchamber latch, "I—I have something I want to tell you."

"Yes?"

"I . . . I got terribly sick again . . . over Keith. I was so ashamed," he confessed.

"Don't be, 'tis perfectly normal," his father replied.

"To be sick?" Greg wondered.

The doctor nodded firmly. "Yes, to be . . . quite sick." He put his hands upon the boy's shoulders again. "Many surgeons are sick at every operation and all of us sometimes, I doubt not. Gregory, I'm proud of you!" Color flooded across the boy's face. "You should be a fine surgeon someday, for you've good judgment and a quality of mercy beyond the ordinary, God bless you! Go to bed now, you're tired; and if you must cry a little, be not ashamed!"